Prepared by the Employment and
Related Services Division
Department of Indian Affairs and
Northern Development

Northern Survival

Fitzhenry & Whiteside

Revised edition

© Minister of Supply and Services Canada 1979

No part of this publication may be reproduced
in any form or by any means without
permission in writing from the publisher.

Fitzhenry & Whiteside Limited
150 Lesmill Road
Don Mills, Ontario M3B 2T5

Consultant to the revised edition

Mike Exall, Coordinator
Centre for Outdoor Pursuits
Seneca College

Canadian Cataloguing in Publication Data

Canada. Dept. of Indian Affairs and Northern
Development.
    Northern survival

Bibliography: p.105
ISBN 0-88902-555-X

1. Wilderness survival — Arctic regions.
I. Title.

SK606.C36 1979   613.6'9'0911
C79-094442-1

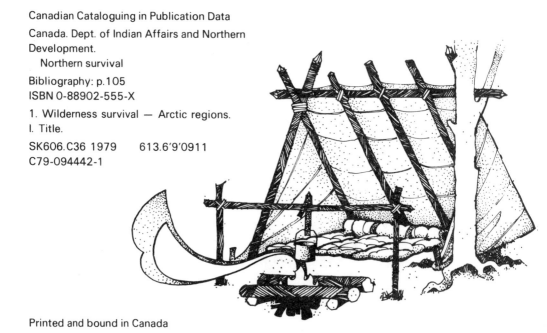

Printed and bound in Canada

Contents

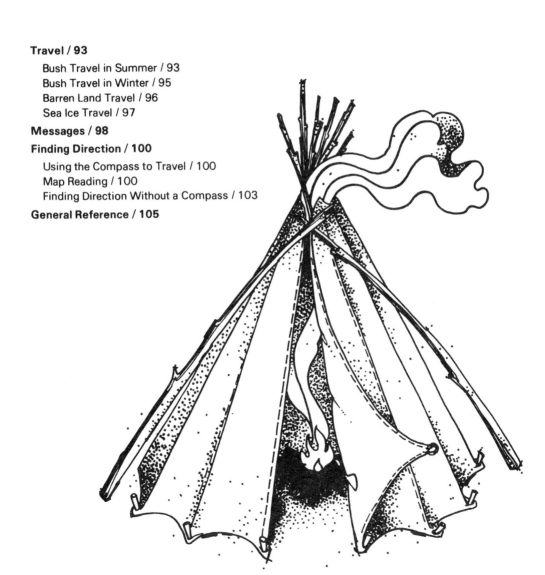

The Hub
of
the North

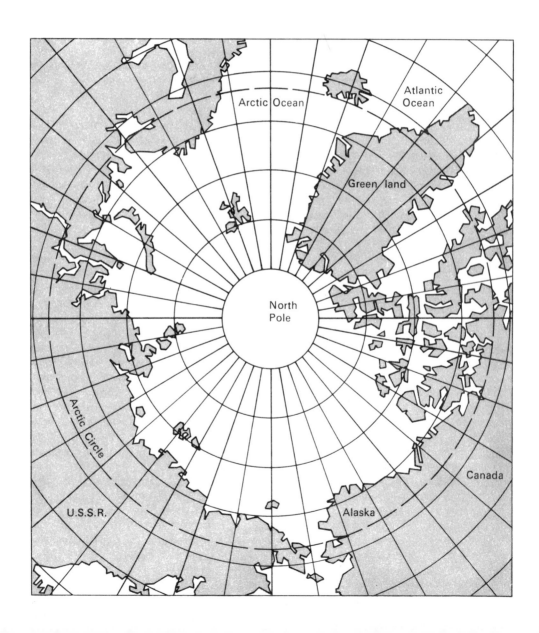

Foreword

With the gradual development of our last
frontier, the Canadian North, more and more
people are travelling east and west, north
and south over this great barren and sometimes hostile land. Travel in the north as
elsewhere has undergone extensive and
dramatic changes within the last decade.
Long distances are covered by aircraft and
the romantic dog sled is being replaced by
skidoos, bombardiers and other power-
driven over-snow vehicles. The increase in
the number of people travelling, the contin-
uing lack of good communications and
severe weather conditions indicates that it
is necessary for all to be as knowledgeable
as possible in survival techniques.

"Northern Survival" was originally developed
in 1967 through the involvement and co-
operation of many people such as Mr. Innes
Taylor of Whitehorse who had first-hand
knowledge and experience in northern
Canadian living.

I would like to thank J. Lawrence Caverhill,
Head, Post School Research and Development of the Employment and Related Services Division for the revision.

G. D. Cromb,
Director, Education Branch.

Planning for Survival

The first steps toward survival in the north should be taken before you ever venture into a wilderness area. A variety of simple precautions undertaken before you set out on any trip can make the difference between life and death if an accident or emergency situation should arise. These fall under five main headings:

- knowledge
- clothing
- food
- equipment
- medical supplies

The importance of the last four items cannot be stressed too much, but it is the first heading that is crucial, as proper knowledge of the situation can remedy deficiencies in the other areas and compensate for mishaps and accidents that otherwise might have serious consequences.

Knowledge

This heading covers two areas. Knowledge of survival techniques is crucial to anyone travelling in the north and they are the subject of this book. It is equally important, however, that someone else should know that you are travelling in a wilderness area, so that your absence can be reported if you do not show up on time. Before setting out on any trip make sure that someone knows where your party is going, the route you intend to follow, and when you expect to return.

Clothing

Even if you expect to be gone only a short time, and to be travelling serenely above bush or tundra in an airplane, you should dress properly for wilderness conditions, with sturdy hiking or work boots and proper shirt and trousers. The weather may be fine when you leave, but take along an extra sweater and a raincoat just in case, and don't forget a hat to give protection from rain, wind and sun. Winter conditions, of course, demand full parka, gloves, insulated footwear and underclothing.

Food

If you travel regularly in wilderness areas, keep a box of emergency supplies in your plane, boat, snowmobile or other vehicle. These may be ordinary tinned goods or specially-prepared lightweight foods designed for wilderness travel. Even a couple of chocolate bars or boxes of raisins may turn out to be crucial.

Equipment

Knife, pocket compass, maps, waterproofed matches, candles, a ball of twine or wire, a few fish hooks and a length of line — these simple items weigh only a few grams but if you have them along they will go far toward making wilderness survival possible. Other items to consider are a saw, axe, or hatchet, a snow knife, a hunting rifle, and a cook kit. And don't forget your sleeping bag — experienced bush pilots never fly without one stowed away somewhere in the plane.

Medical Supplies

Basic first aid procedures are outlined in this book, along with suggestions for maintaining normal health and fitness over a longer period of time in the wilderness. For more details you might consider obtaining a St. John's Ambulance or Red Cross first aid manual, and a properly equipped first aid kit.

Psychological Aspects of Survival

Man, in attempting to conquer outer space has made many advances in the development of clothing, equipment, rations for survival and the techniques for their use. In spite of all these new developments, man when faced with a survival situation still has himself to contend with.

One of the most important of the functional relations which exist between the body and the mind is the ability to accept at once the reality of a new emergency and react in a proper manner to it. Self confidence is important in handling fear and panic and the knowledge of survival information serves to lessen fear and prevent panic from developing.

The normal reaction for any person faced with an emergency or when any of his needs are threatened is one of fear. Fear influences man's behaviour and thus his chances of survival. Fear may lessen a man's chances of survival or he may actually improve under its influence.

The reaction to fear is dependent upon the manner in which a person has trained himself to accept fear. Fear must be recognized, lived with and if at all possible made use of.

Helplessness and hopelessness are two factors which increase fear. Confidence in the equipment, the knowledge and the ability to handle that equipment and concentration on the job to be done will help to control fear.

Pain, cold, thirst, hunger, fatigue, boredom and loneliness are seven enemies of survival. We have all experienced these but few have known them to the extent where our survival has been threatened.

Pain is nature's way of informing a person that something is wrong. It may go unnoticed if your mind is on plans of survival. Pain if surrendered to will weaken the desire to survive.

Cold is a much greater threat to survival than it sounds. It lowers the ability to think and the will to perform and do anything other than become warm.

Thirst, even when not extreme may dull the mind. As with pain and cold if the will to survive is strong enough, thirst can be almost forgotten.

Hunger caused by the lack of food is dangerous in that it lessens a person's ability for rational thought. Both thirst and hunger increases a person's susceptibility to the weakening effects of cold, pain and fear.

Fatigue, even in a moderate amount may reduce one's mental ability. It can make a person careless until the point is reached whereby he does not care to survive. Fatigue may be caused by over-exertion or due to hopelessness, the lack of a goal, frustration and boredom and becomes a manner of escape from a situation which is too difficult to face.

Boredom and loneliness are two difficult enemies to overcome. These feelings creep upon you when things fail to happen or show up.

Attitudes for Survival

A person's chances of having a proper attitude to survive are attained by training and drilling for survival. The mental attitude that *"it can't happen to me"* is dangerous in that the individual will not accept the situation as it exists and is blind to reality. A great number of incidents have been recorded which indicate that previous rehearsal, both mental and actual, of emergency procedures usually result in automatic action on the part of individuals.

Failure to have an attitude of survival may result in panic, even in a person who usually appears calm and collected.

Group Behaviour in Survival

A crew's chances of surviving are largely due to the ability to organize action. While an emergency might be expected to weld a crew together, unless a leader attempts to plan and organize, panic usually takes over.

Group morale may be helped by the realization that a person's survival depends on others whom he trusts. The group can meet with greater persistency and formulate goals to help each other face the future.

Personality Requirements of Survival

The personality of a person may have more to do with survival than danger, weather, terrain or the nature of the emergency. The following qualities are important:

1 can keep cool, calm and collected
2 the ability to make up his mind
3 the ability to improvise
4 the ability to live by himself
5 the ability to adapt to a situation
6 hope for the best, but prepare for the worst
7 have patience
8 ability to take it
9 ability to figure out the other man's thoughts
10 ability to realize where special fears and worries come from and how they may be suppressed.

Physical Aspects of Survival

Survival Priorities

The fundamental physical priorities of a wilderness survivor, whether that person be lost, stranded by a faulty boat or vehicle, or the victim of an air crash, are, in approximate order of urgency:

● first aid
● food and water
● shelter and warmth
● signals to attract rescue

In any survival situation success will depend on the ability of the people involved to provide these fundamental needs for themselves.

Circumstances will vary greatly between such extremes as, for example, a party of well-equipped hikers or canoeists who become lost in summer weather, and the survivors of an air crash in the high arctic under winter conditions.

Despite this extreme range of potential situations, it is hoped that the general sequence of priorities suggested above will be of help as a starting point for northern survivors in analyzing their problems, establishing priorities, and directing their efforts toward surviving in the particular situation that is facing them. As well, the organization of the book is planned to follow this sequence of priorities.

To Go or Not to Go
After the basic physical necessities have been taken care of, survivors, particularly crew and passengers of a downed aircraft, face an important decision — whether to stay near the aircraft or to leave. The distance travelled may be short, involving the search for a good, safe, dry location for a camp, or for a prominent location where you are more apt to be spotted by rescuers. Or the distance to be travelled may be long, perhaps even involving an attempt to walk out to a settlement or major road.

An examination of survival incidents, by both the RCAF and the USAF, indicates that travel is not recommended. Travel in unfamiliar wilderness is usually difficult, dangerous and demanding. If any of the following five basic requirements cannot be fulfilled in your specific situation, don't travel.

a) Know where you are and where you are going. If you do not know where you are, you can rarely plan a route to safety. Stay put!

b) Have a means of setting and maintaining direction. If you have a hand compass and know how to use it, you should be able to maintain a planned course. If you are unable to maintain such a course, remain where you are.

c) Most people are inclined to over-estimate their physical abilities. Be very careful when trying to estimate your physical stamina and if in doubt, don't start out.

d) Clothes make the man. This is particularly true in survival when the proper clothing can mean the difference between life and death. Make certain you are adequately clothed to give protection from the elements and insects. Adequate shoes and heavy socks are most essential. Unless your clothing is sufficient to protect you against conditions which you may encounter, sit and wait.

e) Food, fuel, shelter and signals must be considered in relation to the type of country and the season. If these are available in the area in which you are and you are unable to carry these with you, it is much better to remain where you are.

First Aid

Inhabitants have lived within the Arctic for thousands of years and have learned the effects of cold, wind, glare, poor sanitation and bad ventilation. For a person to live in the North and to survive if deprived of protection from these elements it is necessary to know the means of dealing with the common hazards.

Man and the Cold

As plants can exist within a limit of temperature so can the organs of the human body only function properly through a narrow range of temperatures. Beyond these limits the body ceases to function or fails to function as effectively as within the range. In order that the body temperature be maintained within this range nature has provided the body with a means of adjusting heat retention and loss. Moisture within the body and the large skin surface are the controls of the body temperature.

The body gives up heat by the excretion of fluids and solids, by evaporation, by radiation and by conduction. Evaporation is by far the most important method. Sweat is given off through the skin and in evaporation heat is lost. Sweating continually takes place all over the body though we may be unaware of it. We are usually aware of perspiration due to exercise or increase in heat. A person perspires on a hot day but may shiver on a cold day to exercise the body to produce heat.

To maintain life under extremely cold conditions we may protect it from exposure by clothing, by shelter or supplying heat; by increasing the calorie intake of food and by exercise.

Hypothermia

This is a condition where the body exists at a subnormal temperature. This can be readily produced with low temperatures, high winds and dampness. It can be easily recognized by a person's resistance to cold and chills recurring even in warm circumstances. These are signals and action should be taken to correct the symptoms. Unconsciousness and death may result as the body is being drained of heat without actual freezing in a local area.

The treatment for hypothermia is accomplished by returning the body temperature to its normal range. The best method is to give the person a hot bath and drying well with a rough towel. Such procedure is seldom possible for survivors after a rescue. The patient should be taken to a shelter and bedded down keeping the body well insulated from the ground. The body may be warmed by placing hot rocks, sand or water around him. These heating units should be wrapped in some insulation to prevent burns to the patient especially if placed inside a sleeping bag.

If you are limited in the number of heating units, place them in the following order: the pit of the stomach, the small of the back, the armpits, the back of the neck, the wrists, and between the thighs and the ankles. While the heating units are being warmed or if not available strip the patient of clothing and place two naked people on each side of the patient keeping them well covered by sleeping blankets.

Massaging the patient will help to raise the body temperature. If the shelter is lower than 70° this should be done through the sleeping bag and by reaching the hand down in the sleeping bag.

If the person is conscious stimulation may be helped by hot drinks. Avoid forcing liquids upon an unconscious person as there is danger of suffocation. In treatment of hypothermia *avoid the use of alcohol* as the surface blood vessels open up allowing warmth to escape even though the patient may feel warmer.

Hypothermia may be avoided by conserving body heat and energy. Make certain that in starting a journey all essentials are included a proper meal has been eaten and clothing has not been permitted to become damp from perspiration or that clothing was damp at the start of journey.

Frostbite

Hypothermia is a prelude to frostbite which is the actual freezing of the living tissue. It is usually experienced by a feeling of numbness of the part affected. The skin will become yellowish-white or blue in appearance, and finally the area becomes inactive.

The medical profession has divided frostbite into three degrees which are based upon the size of the area and depth of the penetration. The first degree is distinguished by the yellowish-white colour and the fact that the area remains elastic. Second and third degree frostbite can only be detected as the thawing takes place. During the thawing process blisters will appear on the second degree frostbites. In third degree freezing, ice will appear on the surface and the area will swell proportionately as the thawing continues. This swelling will discolour as the tissue has been destroyed. In some cases the outer skin will come off and an odour will be noticed. This is the indication of the presence of gangrene.

In treating frostbites of any degree, the first step is to seek shelter. First degree frostbites may be thawed by placing the warm, bare hand over the affected part. Avoid rubbing the area to prevent the breaking of the skin.

Second and third degree frostbites should be treated in a similar manner to hypothermia. The heating units should be placed on the unfrozen areas. Hot drinks should be supplied and a mild form of heat applied to the frozen areas. This may be done by immersing the frozen portion in warm but not hot water or the use of wet compresses. These should be changed frequently as they may freeze to the skin when first applied. If a compress freezes to the skin do not pull off but gently thaw out by using the hand or other compresses.

Care must be exercised with the blisters rising from second degree frostbites. These should not be broken as there is danger of infection causing a delay in healing. These blisters must be given adequate protection if going out in the cold.

If in attempting to thaw a third degree frostbite, ice appears on the surface of the frozen portion avoid breaking it off as it usually results in breaking the surface skin. The pain usually becomes severe as sensitivity is restored to the frozen area. The patient may have to be restrained but the area must be thawed. After the thawing has been completed the area should be covered with sterile bandages. These should be applied in a good quantity and rather firmly. They will be required to absorb considerable matter and may require loosening if swelling occurs. If an arm or leg are the frozen members, circulation may be improved by elevating that member ten to twenty degrees.

Examine the area the day following the thawing and if infection is starting antibiotics should be given if available to keep the infection localized.

Frostbite should be prevented rather than attempt to cure. Everyone must have intelligent respect for the cold. A location where wind velocity of 30 miles per hour at a temperature of 30°F can freeze the human flesh in half a minute, and is no place for either ignorance, carelessness or bragging. In the case of injury there may be some excuse for frostbite but usually it is caused by lack of foresight and planning.

Fingers, feet, ears, nose and cheeks are most susceptible to frostbite. If two or more people are together they should frequently check the visible areas for the yellowish-white colour or numbness. If alone, the face should be twisted from time to time and check to ascertain if any areas are becoming numb. If the feet are becoming numb the toes should be wiggled. Hands may be warmed by placing in the armpits.

Frostbite can be prevented by being prepared for sudden changes in the wind velocity and temperature, dressing for emergency rather than being dependent upon the heater in the aircraft and avoiding over taxing the body's heat producer carelessly. Clothes should be vented to avoid perspiration. Avoid touching metal with bare skin and keep out of head winds.

Snowblindness

Snowblindness is a temporary form of blindness caused by a concentration of direct or reflected sun's rays from fresh snow or ice. It occurs most frequently during the spring and early summer when the sun is high up in the sky. The eyes become very sensitive to the glare and begin squinting and watering. The vision ranges from a pink to a red and the eyes appear to have sand and then ground glass in them. If nothing is done to correct the situation vision will be blanked out completely and the person will be in excruciating pain for three or four days.

The person suffering from snowblindness should be placed in a dark room or have eyes covered with a blindfold. Cool compresses may be administered followed by Skyrotien being placed on the inside of the eyelid.

Again prevention is preferred to cure. The wearing of sunglasses or goggles fabricated from cloth, wood or paper but not from metal is recommended. The same precaution must be taken even when the sky is overcast.

Sunburn and Windburn

All exposed parts of the body are subject to sun and windburn. The higher the altitude the more effective is the sun on the skin and the wind combines with the sun to aggravate the situation.

Oily lotions and suntan oils will help prevent the skin from drying out. Failing to have these on hand the use of oils from fresh animal fats such as seal, walrus are useful in an emergency. These should be applied the night before as they increase the heat dissipation. *The best prevention in survival is minimum exposure.*

Shock

Preventative measures may be taken against all the evils of exposure but not so with shock. Shock is apt to occur after an accident and may appear in two forms. The one involves panic, hysteria, mental anxiety and confusion. The other is the result of body injury such as a wound, broken bones, burns, etc. It is recognized by a quickening of the respiration, a pallor of the skin, cold perspiration, confused mental processes, a fast weak pulse or muscle tensions.

Shock is not peculiar to the Arctic, yet cold temperatures make it more difficult to treat. When burns and frostbites occur the plasma oozes from the injured surfaces and if internal injury occurs there is a decrease in the amount of blood in the system. This deprives the heart of its normal supply of blood and thus the extremities are more susceptible to cooling down and freezing. The cooling of the extreme regions of the body has a tendency for the blood to return to the vital organs thus aggravating the situation.

Treatment for such a condition is similar to that of hypothermia, to restore the body to its normal temperature by protection from the cold, applying external heat and massaging the body.

Shock in the more or less dazed form should be treated with sympathy. All the able bodied people should recognize that after any accident or crash the treatment of those suffering shock should be humane and understanding rather than harshful and critical.

Diarrhea
While diarrhea is not peculiar to the Arctic it often besets survivors. It can be serious in that it lowers a person's resistance and defecation is no small problem. The best treatment for diarrhea is to drink plenty of liquids to replace those quantities disposed of by the bowels.

Diarrhea can be prevented and even somewhat controlled by relieving mental strain and maintaining as high a degree of sanitation as possible by cleaning all cooking and eating utensils thoroughly and boiling any water used for drinking. The amount of fat and rich foods consumed should be in very small quantities.

A person should not be concerned if they go a week or longer without any defecation. This is usually due to the limited intake of rough food and the tension experienced in attempting to survive. When food becomes available after discovering an aircraft drop or after rescue only small quantities of food should be taken at any one time to avoid discomfort.

Carbon Monoxide Poisoning
This is a deadly gas resulting from incomplete combustion of synthetic fuels. It may be fatal if found in the air in concentrations greater than four hundreds of one per cent. It is colourless, odorless and tasteless bringing on headaches, drowsiness, nausea, followed by unconsciousness and death in a very short time.

Carbon monoxide gas poisoning can be prevented by maintaining good ventilation at all times, cleaning stoves and carburetors well before they are lighted. Lamps and stoves should never be left burning when sleeping. If ventilation is poor or it is necessary to have heat supplied during the night natural fuels should be used if at all possible. Carbon monoxide burns with a blue flame if complete combustion takes place. If a yellow flame is being generated the stove should be checked.

Personal Hygiene
People who are away from civilization have a tendency to reduce their personal habits of cleanliness. Most of these are relaxed because of the tension in attempting to survive and yet cleanliness is one of the essentials for comfort and warmth of the body.

Perspiration of the body is greater during survival than at other times. If body oils and accumulation of wastes are permitted to build up on the surface of the skin they become conductors of heat which should be retained by the body. This can be removed by the use of a rag a foot square, a bowl of water and some soap. As many of the garments should be removed as possible and the body sponged. If no water is available rubbing the body with a wool rag will have somewhat the same results. It will be found necessary to have such a bath at least once a week.

Another problem which may be experienced while living for prolonged periods in camps is "fur teeth and mouth" trouble. If a tooth brush is not available a piece of cloth on the finger or the finger itself can be used to clean the teeth and massage the gums. A mouthwash of salt and water can be used as a gargle and feathers make excellent toothpicks.

Diseases Present in the North

In the Arctic and Sub-Arctic regions where permafrost exists there is no drainage. Dysentery often exists in areas where native villages have existed for some time. Tuberculosis is still prevalent among the natives in spite of the increased health services. Great care should be exercised in the use of toilet facilities. Drinking water should be boiled or purified with purification tablets.

From Animals

In the north three parasitic diseases exist in some animals which may be transmitted to man. The hare or rabbit may have a disease called tularemia. Care must be asserted in cleaning these as infection from the animal may be transmitted through a cut or open sore. Trichinosis is a disease found in pigs in many parts of the world. The bear is also a carrier of this disease. Hydatid is a parasite carried by the dog, fox, wolf and moose. In all cases the meat of these animals may be consumed without danger if the meat has been well cooked. Some fresh water fish may be heavily infested with tape worm. Most salt water fish may be eaten raw but it is much better to cook the flesh well.

First Aid Following an Accident

The general objectives to first aid should be to preserve life, to minimize the effects of injury, to prevent further injury, and to relieve pain and distress. On no account is a first aid worker expected to do the work of a nurse or a qualified doctor. He should carry out his duties to sustain life and alleviate suffering until qualified medical care can take over. In order to do this it is necessary to work quietly and calmly to provide the injured with assurance that all is not lost. On no account should he rush frantically around looking for ready-made first aid materials but begin at once to improvise with what is at hand.

Before carrying out first aid treatment, it is necessary to determine what is wrong with the injured. The injured should be asked to tell where he is hurt. A systematic procedure should be developed to examine the casualties:

1 look for bleeding to indicate wounds.

2 feel the scalp for bumps to determine possible concussion.

3 check if the injured is able to raise his head and move his neck. This will determine if the neck has been broken.

4 request the injured to lift each arm and leg separately. If a limb cannot be moved, run a hand gently along each member checking for areas of tenderness or swelling. This will usually pinpoint the broken area.

5 ask the injured to take a deep breath and cough. If this can be done without pain he is unlikely to have broken ribs or serious chest injury.

6 ask him to pull in his stomach and blow it out again. If no distress is experienced he is likely free from internal injury.

7 without moving or lifting the casualty run a firm hand down the centre of his back. A tender spot may mean a broken spine.

Note: If a first aid worker suspects an injured person to have a broken spine or neck, do not attempt to lift the casualty. He should be carefully slid to some type of stretcher. (See improvisations.)

In examining an injured person, it may be necessary to remove some clothing. Do not remove or destroy clothing unnecessarily, but if further access to a part is essential, do not hesitate to cut the clothing sufficiently for the purpose. When removing jacket, shirt, or trousers, always slip garment off the sound limb first, then off the injured limb.

Wounds
The first principle which should be impressed is that the first aiders should not apply tourniques or waste time trying to locate the allusive "pressure spots". Wounds that are likely to happen on the trail may be single or multiple, large or small, deep or shallow, ragged or cleancut, depending whether they are caused by knives, bullets, shotguns, ice, abrasions, can opener, dog bite or mauling by polar bears, or other means. The principle of first aid management of wounds is virtually always as follows: 1 *Control bleeding*. 2 *Prevent infection*.

1 Control of Bleeding
It is important to appreciate that the bleeding from most wounds will stop spontaneously even though no treatment whatever is given. Nature has two highly effective methods of minimizing blood loss:

a) *Retraction of Vessels.* Blood vessels, when cut across, promptly pull back into the tissues and shrink in diameter because of "elastic" fibres in their walls. At the same time the inner layer of the vessel wall curls back into itself and thus tend to block the tube. These blood vessel reactions are surprisingly effective so that it is not unusual to see patients with quite large wounds who have lost relatively little blood.

b) *Clotting of Blood.* As soon as blood escapes from the vessels in which it is normally contained it undergoes the phenomenon of "clotting" by which it changes from a liquid to a jelly. Substances released from damaged tissue tend to accelerate this process, which ordinarily occurs in from three to seven minutes. Blood clot seals the open vessels and plugs the wound, thereby preventing further bleeding.

By three simple measures the first aider can help Nature to stop bleeding:

1 *Rest.* If the casualty is encouraged to lie down quietly and particularly to keep the wounded part still, his blood pressure will drop, his pulse will become slow, and the amount of blood flowing into the wounded area will diminish. All of these factors will help to minimize the loss of blood from the wound.

2 *Elevation.* Blood, like water, does not readily run uphill. If it is possible to elevate the wounded arm or leg, or head, above the level of the heart, bleeding will be diminished and will stop more quickly.

3 *Pressure.* The application of firm pressure directly on the wound is by far the most important method of controlling hemorrhage. Ordinarily pressure is applied through a dressing which is bandaged firmly on the wound. The dressing should be thick and compressible to facilitate the application of even pressure over the whole wound area.

A firm dressing reduces bleeding by compressing all blood vessels leading into the wound and so lessens blood flow and retains shed blood in the wound until clotting occurs.

If bleeding is not quickly controlled by a properly applied dressing, put on more pressure:

a) by adding a further dressing on the outer side of the first and bandaging more tightly (i.e., "reinforcing the dressing")

b) or by pressing on the dressing with the palm of the hand. In cases of profuse bleeding, when a dressing is not immediately available, it is permissible to press with the bare hand directly on the bleeding point. The exact site of maximum pressure can be altered until the effective position is found.

If such pressure is maintained for ten minutes by the clock it will almost always be found possible to replace the hand with a snugly applied dressing. *If sufficient pressure is applied to the wound, bleeding will always be controlled.*

Here we accept the risk of introducing germs into the wound; but if the rapid bleeding is not stopped, the casualty may die.

Very occasionally, in a wound of arm or leg involving a large artery, bleeding is so rapid and forceful that it can be controlled only by constant pressure with the hand over the cut vessel. For such cases the first aider must move with the casualty to the hospital so that the vital pressure may be maintained without interruption.

Note: If bleeding cannot be suppressed by the above methods a tourniquet may be necessary but should be used as a last resort.

The loss of large amounts of blood will lead to pallor, weakness, collapse, unconsciousness, and death. In such cases, after control of hemorrhage, it is necessary at the earliest opportunity to replace by transfusion the blood which has been lost.

Persons who are believed to have lost large amounts of blood must be taken as quickly as possible to a hospital or other institution where blood transfusions can be given.

2 Prevention of Infection

Infection means the growth of harmful germs in a wound. Within a few hours or days the wound which is infected becomes red and angry looking ("inflamed"), swollen, hot, increasingly painful, and may discharge pus. Healing is delayed. The patient may feel sick with headache, feverishness, chills, aches and pains. Spread of the infection to deeper tissues or to blood stream ("blood poisoning"), may lead to serious illness or even death.

Until recent years infection was the commonest complication of wounds and the most frequent cause of death from wounds. Improvements in first aid and surgical treatment, and the introduction of penicillin and other antibiotics have been responsible for greatly reducing the incidence of serious wound infections. *To prevent infection in wounds we must keep germs out.* We can best accomplish this objective if we understand clearly how germs get into wounds. There are just two ways by which germs can enter wounds.

1 Some germs may be embedded in the wound by the knife, bullet, rusty nail or other object which causes the injury. The problem with these "embedded" germs is how to remove them.

2 Some germs may be implanted in the wound after the original injury. These come from two main sources:

a) the noses and throats of persons who breathe, talk, cough or sneeze into the wound (i.e., droplet infection).

b) the skin of careless first aiders, nurses, or doctors, who allow their fingers to enter or touch the wound.

The problem with these "implanted" germs is how to kill them in the wound.

We can now understand that there are two methods of preventing infection:

1 Removal of germs embedded in the wound at time of injury: Complete removal of these embedded germs can be accomplished only by the surgeon who, aided by anaesthesia, opens the wound widely and washes it out thoroughly. This procedure should be carried out as soon as possible; every half-hour of delay makes the surgeon's job more difficult and less certain. This again is another reason for getting the casualty to the doctor quickly: *"first aid must not delay first treatment".*

However, when circumstances permit it to be done promptly, as in many peace-time accidents, the first aider may help by washing out the wound with a large quantity of sterile water. Cool boiled water is preferable but, in municipalities with water purification systems, tap water is acceptable.

2 Protection of wound against germs being implanted after the injury: This is the main objective of first aid in relation to wound infection. It is readily accomplished: Cover the wound as quickly as possible with a sterile or clean dressing and keep it covered. Before applying the dressing, if possible, wash your hands carefully. It is also advisable, under ideal circumstances, to wash off the skin around the wound with soap and warm water.

While applying the dressing, do not breathe, talk, cough, or sneeze into or over the wound. Either cover your mouth and nose with a "mask", (i.e., clean handkerchief), or keep your face turned slightly away from the wound until the dressing is in place. Keep fingers out of the wound. Do not touch the surface of the dressing which will be placed next to the wound.

Foreign Bodies in Wound

Large foreign bodies, such as fragments of glass or metal, if projecting from the wound may be gently removed, providing this can be done without putting fingers into the wound.

Antiseptics

It should be emphasized that "antiseptics" are almost completely ineffective in killing or removing germs embedded in a wound. The chief result of introducing these strong chemicals into a wound is to cause unnecessary pain and to damage the exposed tissues. For this reason iodine and other antiseptics have no place in first aid and should not, under any circumstances, be poured into or on a wound.

Complicated Wounds

1 If the casualty is coughing blood, as from a lung wound, set him up with his head supported.
2 If the casualty is vomiting blood, as from a damaged stomach, bend his knees and make him as comfortable as possible.
3 For chest wounds, make the wound airtight.
4 For abdominal wounds, give nothing by mouth.

Fractures

A fracture is a broken bone.

Diagnosis of Fracture. It is important to be able to recognize a fracture. In many cases there is no difficulty.

The following are indications of fracture: The injured person says that he heard or felt the bone snap, or the limb is bent in a way that could only occur if the bone were broken (i.e., "Deformity").

In other cases the diagnosis of "fracture" must be made on more indirect evidence:

1 Unusually severe pain which is made worse if either casualty or first aider tries to move the injured part.

2 Marked tenderness on pressing gently with the fingers over the exact site of fracture along a bone. Even a few inches away from this point the tenderness caused by light pressure will be much diminished.

3 Unnatural mobility is noted, i.e., the limb seems to bend at some place other than a normal joint.

4 Swelling usually occurs rapidly but is not reliable as an early sign of fracture.

In many cases the diagnosis of fracture can be made with certainty only by means of an X-ray examination. Hence – *when in doubt treat as a fracture.*

General Principles of First Aid for Fractures

Every unnecessary movement of the sharp ends of a broken bone causes extra pain and increases damage to surrounding tissues, muscles may be lacerated, blood vessels may be cut, nerves may be injured. The sole objective of first aid for fractures is to avoid these complications by *immobilization,* which means "to fix the injured part in such a way as to minimize movement at the site of fracture".

Immobilization is accomplished by applying a splint, i.e., "a rigid support for the broken bone". There are many types of splints, for example:
a) an uninjured portion of the casualty's body, e.g., the opposite leg, or trunk.

b) a prepared metal or wooden splint.

c) an improvised splint – wooden slats, rifle or shotgun (unloaded), axe handle, gaff, fish spear, harpoon.

d) a stretcher on which the casualty lies, e.g., in the case of a broken back or neck.

e) the casualty's own muscles – most important in the mouth, the muscles surrounding and attached to a broken bone may be amazingly effective in producing immobilization. Therefore, as will be explained later, external splinting is unnecessary in certain types of fracture.

Rules for Splinting Fractures

2a) If a splint is necessary, apply it before moving the injured person, i.e., "splint them where they lie". Of course, it is not always possible to adhere strictly to this rule as it may be necessary to move the casualty out of danger before first aid can be carried out.

b) If possible while applying a splint have the injured limb supported very steadily by an assistant. The simplest and most effective way of steadying a broken arm or leg is to pull firmly on hand or foot, i.e., "Traction" This stretches the muscles tightly around the broken bone thus straightening it and steadying it at the same time. Only while traction is being applied is it possible to apply splints and bandages without causing extra pain or producing further damage.

c) Fasten the limb to the splint securely by bandages above and below the fracture and at either end of the splint. Bandages should be carefully "snugged up" to hold the injured limb firmly without being so tight as to be uncomfortable or to run the risk of shutting off the circulation of blood.

d) Use padding as necessary to fill in the hollow between the straight splint and the normal curves of the injured limb and also to avoid uncomfortable pressure against protruding bony points as on outer side of ankle, hip or elbow.

Management of Open ("Compound") Fractures

The wound and the broken bone must each be dealt with in the usual way:
1 Steady the fracture (usually by traction).
2 Dress the wound.
3 Splint the fracture.

In the occasional case where the broken bone is protruding from the wound, do not make any attempt to pull or push it back under the skin. Just cover it with a dressing and try to keep the injured limb as steady as possible until the casualty reaches hospital.

Examples of First Aid Treatment for Fractures

The general principles outlined above may be readily adapted to the management of fractures of the various bones:

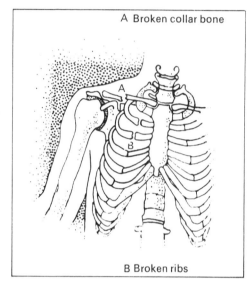

A Broken collar bone

B Broken ribs

"Broken collar bone" is one of the commonest of all fractures. It is usually caused by a fall on the outstretched hand. The injured person holds his arm rigidly against the side of his chest and complains of pain on any movement. If the first aider runs his fingers gently along the collar bone he will come to one spot which is very tender.

The muscles attached to this bone will keep it adequately splinted provided the arm is not moved. First aid is, therefore, simple.
1 Place a small pad in the armpit and bind upper arm to the side of the chest.
2 Put the forearm in a sling.

Hand or Foot. Fractures of the small bones in hand or foot, fingers or toes, do NOT require any first aid splinting. An injured hand should be cradled in a sling. A person with a fracture of the foot will be unable to walk and so will require some form of hand carriage or transportation.

Wrist and Forearm. "Broken wrist" like "broken collar bone" is a very common injury. It, too, is usually the result of a fall on the outstretched hand. Fractures of the shaft, of the forearm bones are more commonly produced by a direct blow somewhere between elbow and wrist. Casualties who have broken wrist or forearm are usually found carefully supporting the injured limb with their other hand. Visible deformity, marked tenderness over the site of fracture and unwillingness to use the arm and hand, make the diagnosis easy.

First aid is as follows:
1 Steady the injured forearm by traction, i.e., firm pull between fingers and elbow.
2 Apply splint from knuckles to elbow.

Upper Arm. Diagnosis is usually not difficult. The injured person holds the arm against his side and complains of severe pain on the slightest movement or touch.

Nature has provided for this fracture a splint which is always available – the side of the chest. Hence, to give first aid,
1 Place a soft pad between upper arm and chest wall.

2 Fasten the arm against the side of the chest by bandage or adhesive tape or by pinning the sleeve to the vest or jacket.
3 Put the forearm in a sling.

Thigh Bone. This is the largest bone in the body. A fractured femur is always a serious injury. Fracture of the upper end of the femur is usually called "a broken hip" – it is commonly caused by a simple fall in old people whose bones have become fragile and brittle. The casualty says, "I have a bad pain in my hip"; the limb cannot be moved; the leg tends to roll outwards so the foot points outward while the opposite foot points forward. In many cases the injured limb appears shortened. Fracture of the shaft of the femur can be produced only by powerful force as may occur in falls from a height, explosions, or by penetrations – such things as bullets.

Persons with this injury have great pain and are quite unable to use the affected leg. There is marked tenderness usually sharply localized over the site of fracture. In some cases deformity is not apparent. The thigh quickly becomes swollen. First aid for thigh fractures must be prompt and precise:

1 Steady the fracture by traction, i.e., have an assistant pull steadily but firmly on the foot, keeping the toes pointed upwards.

2 Immobilize by either of following methods:
a) bind injured limb to sound limb by bandages about upper thigh, above and below knee, around ankle and foot;
b) apply a long rigid splint such as a wooden slat to the outer side of the limb from sole of foot to lower part of chest. Fasten splint securely with bandages around lower chest, hips, upper thigh, above and below the knee, ankle and foot.

3 Carefully lift the casualty to a stretcher and evacuate to hospital.

Shin-bone. Since this is a large bone covered with relatively little muscle, diagnosis fracture is seldom in doubt. Deformity is frequently apparent and localized tenderness to gentle pressure over the "break" can readily be detected. First aid as follows:

1 Have an assistant steady the leg by traction on the foot.

2 Splint – two useful methods are suggested:
a) a sleeping bag or blanket wrapped firmly around leg, ankle to foot, and fastened with safety pins or bandaged securely. This makes an effective and comfortable splint.

b) wooden splints, preferably on both sides of the leg, from sole of foot to upper thigh, fastened by bandages above and below knee, and at either end of splint.

3 Transport for treatment.

Ankle. A violent "twisting of the ankle" frequently results in fracture of one or more of the bones close to the joint. There is severe pain and usually marked swelling of the ankle. Most persons with this injury cannot walk, but a few will limp about in great distress. The injury is usually described as a "badly sprained ankle" until an X-ray examination establishes the correct diagnosis.

As far as first aid is concerned this type of fracture may be treated merely by transporting the casualty on a stretcher to the nearest medical aid. If the trip is likely to be long or bumpy, increased comfort may be obtained by wrapping folded blankets around the foot and ankle and fastening it securely with safety pins or bandages.

Ribs. These are usually broken by a crushing injury of the chest in which the ribs crack like barrel staves which have been bent too far. Less frequently rib fractures may be caused by a direct blow on the chest wall as, for example, in a fall against the corner of a table. The person who has broken ribs will complain of pain on breathing deeply and especially on coughing. Occasionally, if the underlying lung has been damaged, a small amount of blood may be coughed up. There is no effective means of first aid splinting for this injury. The casualty should be put at rest upon a stretcher and taken to a hospital or doctor's office. If his breathing seems difficult, some relief may be obtained by propping him up in a semi-sitting position.

Spine ("Broken Back" or "Broken Neck"). Fracture of the neck most commonly occurs as a result of diving accidents in which the head strikes an unsuspected shallow bottom. Another mechanism by which this injury may be produced is the sharp snapping of the passenger's head forward or back when a speeding automobile, plane, or train, crashes to a sudden stop.

Broken back is usually caused by falls from a height with the victim landing on his back, feet, or buttocks. The injury may also be produced by a heavy weight (e.g., falling tree, or masonry) striking the casualty so that he is bent forward in a sudden violent manner.

The person with a fractured spine usually has such pain in his back and neck that he is literally "afraid to move". Remember that *any careless movement of the broken bones may crush the spinal cord and produce permanent paralysis and loss of sensation.* This is one injury in which the first aider must not hurry but proceed slowly and with care and caution:

1 get two or three assistants and instruct them carefully.

2 the casualty must be moved on to a firm, flat stretcher, (an improvised stretcher, such as a door, wide board, shutter, sled, etc., will do quite well) keeping his neck and back stiff and straight, and taking great care to avoid bending or twisting him. If damage to the spinal cord has already occurred, the casualty will be unable to move his feet and legs (i.e., "paralysis") or to appreciate when his skin is touched in that area, (i.e., "loss of sensation").

Burns
A "Burn" is the damage to body tissues caused by exposure to extreme heat. Burns vary in their "depth" and the "area" of body surface involved. The "depth" of a burn is important:

a) *"Superficial" burns* – Only the outer layers of the skin are damaged. The burned area looks fiery red and may become blistered. There is very severe pain. Healing is rapid and leaves little scar.

b) *"Deep" burns* – Full thickness of skin is destroyed and underlying fat and muscle burned to varying depths. The burned area usually has a yellowish-white "cooked" appearance. There is less pain because nerves in the skin have been destroyed. Healing is slow and often results in disfiguring scars.

The "Area" of a burn is even more important: The immediate outcome of a burn is determined by its area. The larger the area burned the more seriously ill the casualty will become. Any burn, even though superficial, involving one third or more of the body surface may result in dangerous illness. If one half or more of the skin is involved, death will frequently ensue.

Types of Burn
The characteristics of any particular burn are determined by its cause. Contact with red hot metal will cause a sharply localized burn which may be quite deep.

a) *A fire burn* – clothes on fire, flaming gasoline, or caught in a burning building – usually involves a large area of the body and in some places is quite deep. Charred clothing is often stuck to the burned surface.

b) *A scald* is a burn caused by steam, boiling water, or other hot liquid; it is generally quite superficial but may be extremely serious if a large part of body is involved.

c) *Chemical burns* are caused by strong acids or caustics that can quickly damage skin on which they are spilled or splashed. Burning will continue until the offending chemical is either washed away by water or neutralized by the appropriate antidote.

First Aid for Burns

Unfortunately first aid measures for dealing with burns are rather limited. There is no effective way of relieving the agonizing pain of extensive burns except by morphine or other hypodermic sedative.

When the burn is confined to part of one limb, such as one hand or one foot, some lessening of the pain may be achieved by immersing the injured area in cold water. Unless medical attention seems imperative it is safe to continue cold treatment until the phase of severe pain is past, usually one to two hours.

Serious Burns, any burn covering an area greater than that of an eight inch square, and all deep burns.
1 Remove or cut away clothing over burned area but do *not* attempt to pull off clothing which is stuck.
2 Cover burned area with sterile or clean dressing and bandage or fasten securely.
In case of burns covering a large part of the body, it is sufficient to cover the area with a clean sheet or towel.
3 If the casualty is thirsty, he may be allowed to drink small amounts of clear fluids such as water or tea.
4 Place on stretcher and evacuate quickly to hospital.

Do not put Vaseline, burn ointment or any greasy substance on serious burns. These remedies have only slight value in reducing pain while they greatly complicate the surgical treatment of the burned area.

Chemical Burns
1 Wash off immediately with large volume of water.
2 Apply neutralizing agent if available.
for acids – solution of baking soda
for caustics – dilute vinegar
3 Put on dressing.

Notes on Rescue of Burn Casualties

When a person's clothing catches fire approach him holding a rug, blanket, or coat in front of yourself for protection, wrap it around him, lay him flat and smother the flames.

In attempting to rescue persons from burning buildings, vehicles or aircraft, observe the following precautions:

1 Cover your nose and mouth with a wet cloth to keep out the superheated air which might burn your lungs.

2 Always feel a door before opening it – if it is hot, open very cautiously to avoid being caught in a blast of flame and hot air.

3 Be conscious of danger of explosion.

Rabies

If during your wanderings in the bush, you notice a wild animal that appears to be sick, or behaves abnormally, showing ferociousness where it would usually show fear, or a dog behaving in an unusual manner and frothing at the mouth, such an animal may have rabies. Foxes normally avoid people; skunks do not usually approach people and try to bite them; on the other hand, squirrels and chipmunks are frequently coaxed to feed from a person's hand and if a bite is inflicted it does not necessarily mean abnormal behaviour or an unprovoked attack.

Prevention and Treatment. Do not pet any wild animal, no matter how tame it may appear to be – lack of fear of humans is a bad sign. If a person is bitten or scratched by, or comes in contact with the saliva of a suspected rabid animal, the affected parts should be thoroughly washed with soap and water for fifteen minutes. If iodine or other antiseptic is available, put it in or around the wound. Get in touch with a doctor as soon as possible.

Water

Water is more necessary to human existence than food. Do not drink sea water as it increases your thirst.

Summer Water Sources. Spring water or fast running water is best but any running water or that from properly drained lakes in isolated areas will be safe. Sometimes when surface water cannot be procured, water can be obtained by digging into moist soil usually in low ground. Other sources are the sap layers of trees such as birch and maple in the spring; dew on plants, rain water and fish juices.

Winter Water Sources. If open water cannot be found, use ice instead of snow. However, hard snow will produce more water than soft fluffy snow. This can be overcome by packing it and then melting. Snow can be eaten if thawed in the hand first and taken when it has a slushy consistency. *Never drink water until certain of its purity.*

Purification of Water
Boil three to five minutes and shake afterwards to restore the oxygen.

Sources of Water
At sea far from land the experienced Arctic traveller uses last year's ice or older for drinking and cooking. It can be distinguished from this year's by the rounded corners which are due to the rains and thaws of the summer. It looks bluish in comparison with salt ice which is milkish in appearance.

In summer you are always certain of fresh water at sea by nipping it up from the hollows in old ice.

In the early fall, fresh water is sometimes found by noting where there is a deep snowdrift covering a hollow. If the snow is two or three feet deep, you may find even two or three months after freeze-up that the ice pond is only a foot or so thick with sufficient quantities of fresh water underneath.

On land the Arctic traveller will by preference chisel down through the surface of a lake or river till fresh water is obtained.

It is perfectly safe to eat snow when you are thirsty but most travellers find it pleasanter to drink water. If no water is obtainable, you eat snow or cracked ice during the day to quench your thirst and at camp time bring indoors chunks of ice which can be cut up for the pot as needed. If ice is not available use great quantities of soft or granular snow.

Plant Food

Water Hemlock. This is the most poisonous plant in Canada.

A Leaves and flowers

Food
Natural Food. Every effort should be made to discover and obtain natural foods within the area so as to conserve your energy, however, there are few calories in edible plants.

Plant Life
Most green plants are a potential source of Vitamin C such as rose hips (the buds of wild roses). Tea can be made by pouring boiling water over labrador tea leaves, spruce tips, willow tips and dandelion leaves.

Anything that is not bitter or anything eaten by birds and animals is probably but not necessarily safe to eat. If doubtful, take minute quantities at first and wait twenty-four hours for a reaction.

Poisonous Plants
There are no poisonous plants north of the tree-line. However, south of the tree-line there are three which can be mistaken for edible plants and can cause death.

Water Hemlock. It grows two to four feet tall. It is the most poisonous plant in Canada. It is a member of the carrot family and has toothed three-part purple streaked leaves which emit a disagreeable odour when crushed and hollow tube-like roots which emit a parsniplike odour. It can be easily confused with Cow Parsnip which is edible.

Death Cup Mushroom (usually 4 to 6 inches tall when mature)

A Note the basal cup
B Mature mushroom
C Over mature mushroom

Red or White Baneberry
Note the characteristic terminal cluster of berries

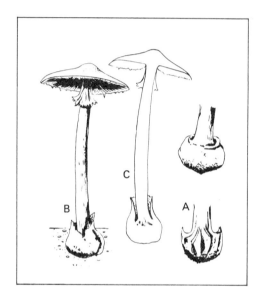

Death Cup Mushroom. This mushroom is found in the wooded areas of northern Canada. It is indistinguishable when young, but in maturity has a soft white cup-line formation at the base and a broad collar-like ring part way up the stem. Avoid all mushrooms having this structure and also mushrooms in the button stage. It has been confused with the common edible mushroom.

Baneberry. This is a bushy perennial, two or three feet tall with small white flowers in a short thick terminal cluster. Red or white berries replace the flowers and resemble dolls' eyes in appearance. The root stalk is substantial. Avoid berries growing in clusters of this type.

Edible Plants

Flowers of most plants in Canada are safe to eat either boiled or raw.

Greens such as dandelion leaves will provide roughage and vitamins. These can be eaten raw or boiled. Some delicious edible greens are: bracken fronds or fiddleheads, the lower tender inner twelve inches of cat-tail or bulrush stalks, young green milkweed pods, young water-lily pods and pigweed.

Roots such as cat-tail, wild carrot and liquorice will provide starch and protein. The roots of the cat-tail are obtainable in both winter and summer and are best boiled. Other common delicious edible roots are bracken, vetch, tiger-lily, ladys' slippers and the tubers of arrowhead plant.

Berries. The edible berries are too numerous to mention. Blue and black berries not in clusters are generally safe. Red and white berries should be avoided unless positively identified to be safe.

Lichens. These are dry scale-like plants, usually found on rocks or old stumps in both the Arctic and wooded areas. They can be boiled and dried, then ground into a powder and stewed for use as a soup thickener. A common edible lichen is the lemon lichen.

Mushrooms. Although some mushrooms are edible, delicious and filling they are not particularly high in nourishment and since some are extremely poisonous they should be left alone unless positively identified as being edible.

Leaves. The leaves of labrador tea, a shrub-like growth on practically all muskeg areas in Canada, can be steeped to produce a stimulating beverage.

Trees. Sap from trees, such as the maple, basswood, birch and poplar, is a source of water with some food value particularly in the spring of the year. At other times the cambium or succulent new growth between the wood and the bark of such common trees as poplar and jack pine can be scraped to produce a pulpy residue which is tasty.

Lichens. There are many varieties of lichens which can be eaten. Some can be nibbled raw but they are generally acidic and should be soaked in water for several hours then removed, dried, and crumbled, before boiling to a gelatinous consistency. May be used effectively in thickening soups, stews, etc., or as a broth.

Bracken. Rootstalks are nutritious but quite woody. Roast or boil.

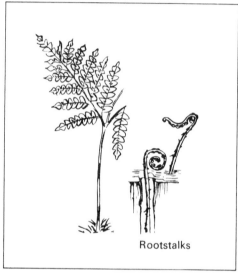

Rootstalks

1 *Cow Parsnip.* Young leaves and flower stalks make a sweet green. Eat raw or boiled.

2 *Woolly Lousewort.* The roots and young flowering stems may be eaten raw or boiled. A common perennial of the Arctic tundra, up to eight inches in height.

3 *Liquorice Root.* A vetch-like plant found in the northern forests and on the tundra. The flowers are pink-purplish and look somewhat like pea blossoms. The roots are quite substantial and can be eaten raw or boiled.

4 *Lamb's Quarters or Pigweed.* Common throughout North America. The young leaves of this plant make an excellent green. Boil like spinach.

1.

3.

2.
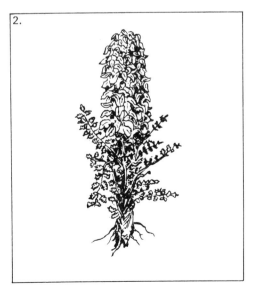

4.

1 *Stinging Nettle.* The leaves of the young plant make an excellent green. The bristled leaves and stems of the mature nettle produce a rash upon contact with the skin. Crushed dock leaves make an effective remedy for nettle stings.

2 *Pond Lily.* Widely distributed, the roots may be eaten if peeled and boiled. The seed pods are best when newly formed. Boil in two changes of water.

3 *Tiger-lily or Turk's Cap Lily.* Has a brown, spotted orange flower. After peeling, the roots may be boiled or eaten raw.

4 *Lady's Slipper.* The roots may be boiled or eaten raw.

5 *Silver-Weed.* Has widespread distribution. The roots are a perfectly acceptable food when boiled or roasted.

1 *Cat-tail.* Grows in marshy or wet ground. The flowering head is edible when young and green. Boil like asparagus.

The white succulent inner portion of the lower 12 to 15 inches of stem is widely used as food. Boil or eat raw.

Roots may be baked, boiled, or roasted. If woody, chew and swallow the starchy material. Spit out the residue.

2 *Nutgrass.* Has a three-angled stem and grows in low ground near water. Peel the root and eat raw or boiled. (Better boiled.) The Ground Nut may be used in a similar manner.

3 *Reindeer-Moss.* A greyish, coral-like plant. Can be powdered and mixed with flour, or boiled to make soup.

1.

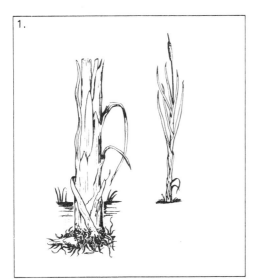

2.

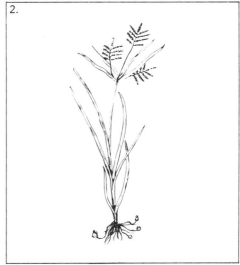

3.

3.

Dandelion. The leaves are an excellent green. The dried, ground-up roots make a substitute for chicory which is a substitute for coffee.

Labrador Tea. Widely distributed. Leaves make an aromatic beverage somewhat like Chinese tea.

Dry the leaves over a fire in a pan until they become crumbly. The infusion is prepared by pouring boiling water over the leaves. The resultant brew is high in vitamin "C".

Animal Food

Animal food will give you the most food value per pound. Anything that creeps, crawls, swims or flies is a possible source of food.

Grasshoppers or Locusts. These are considered to be a delicacy in many countries. It is best to remove the wings and legs and toast the body on a stick.

Grubs. The white wood burrowing larvae of beetles, are usually found in rotten logs. Remove the head, thorax and legs and eat. The eggs are edible if enough can be procured but are dry and tasteless.

Snails. Both aquatic and terrestrial snails are an excellent source of nourishment when obtainable.

Earthworms. The large types particularly, are eaten in many countries.

Reptiles. Lizards, frogs, snakes and turtles are all exceptionally tasty whether boiled or fried.

Game Meat

All Canadian birds and animals are edible except the livers of polar bear and bearded seal. These have an excessive Vitamin A content which produces a toxic reaction.

Hunting and Fishing

To the majority, hunting implies the use of the gun, but there are other productive methods of taking game. The survivor should plan to use every means at his disposal favouring those which will require the least effort to achieve results.

Snares, traps, nylon gill-nets and set lines will work for you day and night. Get them into operation as soon as possible. Make use of any available material and improvise. Scout the area of your landing early to learn its game potential. Tackle the job systematically.

Before departing, establish a base line or check points by which you can always orient yourself in relation to your camp. This could be a river, a lake shore, hill or even a blazed trail north and south to your camp.

Hunting Hints

1 Walk as quietly as possible.

2 Move slowly, stop frequently and listen.

3 Look around.

4 Hunt upwind or crosswind whenever possible.

5 Blend with terrain features as much as possible. Do not stand against the skyline or break from cover without thorough observation.

6 Be prepared – game frequently startles the hunter or catches him off guard.

Watch for:

1 *The animal itself* – don't get excited when you see it; very often it isn't certain what you are and will remain still. Make all movements slowly and make the first shot count.

2 Trails – usually beaten down through heavy usage. If recently used, these trails are excellent for setting snares.

3 Tracks – may provide a wealth of information such as: the type, size, age and sex of the animal; the direction taken; the age of tracks and whether the animal was frightened.

4 Droppings – the best indication of what animal has passed; will sometimes reveal favourite roosting spots of birds.

5 Feeding grounds, water-holes and salt licks are good locations for hunting in the early morning or evening. Trails leading to such places may provide excellent sites for setting snares or traps.

6 Dens, holes and food stores provide good spots for setting snares.

Dressing Game

Some birds, such as ptarmigan and the various species of grouse, can be skinned using the fingers only. Break the skin on the breastbone and work around the body.

Sea birds such as gulls, fish-eating ducks should be skinned to diminish the fishy taste. The craw or first stomach should always be checked as the content if not digested may provide nutritious foods, such as buds, berries and seeds which can be eaten.

Large animals which are too large to elevate may be skinned by starting in the centre of the stomach and skinning to the centre of the back. Spread the skin out on the ground to protect the meat and roll the animal over and skin the other side. All internal organs should be removed immediately to prevent bloating. Big game is usually bled out by the bullet which kills it; however, it is advisable to cut the jugular vein after killing to assure thorough bleeding, hence better tasting and keeping of meat.

Big game is more easily utilized when it has been cut into manageable chunks. Heart, liver and kidneys of all game can be used except as previously mentioned. In the removal of the liver, be careful and not break the gall sack. Incidentally, there is no gall sack in deer or other antlered game.

Small Game

The mainstay of the survivor, particularly if he has no rifle, will likely be small animals and birds. These are well distributed through the Canadian hinterland and may be taken without firearms.

Rabbit There are several species common in Canada. In woodlands they frequent heavy thickets. They are taken in snares set on their runways, preferably where the runway is restricted by natural or man made obstacles. The balance pole snare and the common rabbit snares are shown in the diagrams.

Squirrels. These are common throughout Canada's forests. They store their food in tree cavities, nests or holes in the ground but their food is of little value for human consumption.

The leaning pole snare is a simple effective method of taking squirrels. Three or more snares mounted on a pole leading to their nest or food cache will be most effective.

Mice and Lemming. These are edible and should not be overlooked by the survivor.

1 *Common Rabbit Snare* (Using Wire)
Dead sticks may be inserted into the ground to guide the rabbit into the snare.

A Close-up of the loop. Wires should be twisted together.

2 *Balance Pole Snare* (Using cord)

B This end should be about 4 lbs. heavier than the other end. Make certain that the balance pole will lift the rabbit clear of the ground.

3 Rabbit snares should normally be 4½ inches in diameter and 3 inches from the ground.

C Nicks to hold up the snare.

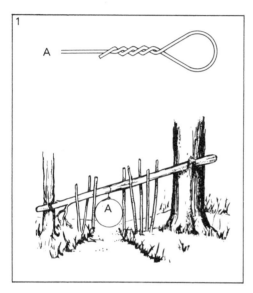

Porcupine. The porcupine is found in most forested areas. Watch for trees with the bark freshly stripped off fairly high above the ground. It can be killed with a club or a spear. Be careful in handling. To skin, open the hide along the belly and peel the hair back over the top of the quills. Work from the inside of the skin to prevent contact with the quills.

Mink, Martin. These are not rated as table delicacies, but if you can shoot, snare or trap them put them in the pot.

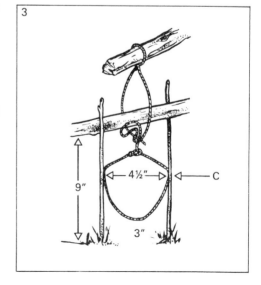

4 *The Leaning Pole Snare.* Three or four snares mounted on a pole leading to their nest or food cache will be effective.

5 Detail of leaning pole snare showing noose on top.

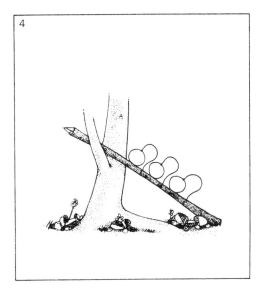

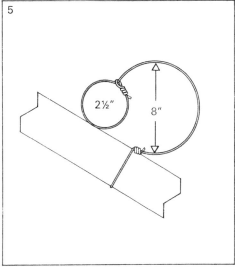

Muskrat and Beaver. The Muskrat is found in pond, slough and marsh areas; the beaver along streams and lakes passing through poplar on willow country. They may be shot while swimming usually in the early morning or late evening. Beavers and muskrats usually maintain paths where snares may be placed. In the early spring and late fall evidence may be found of these animals coming out from under the ice. You may cut one off from the safety of the water.

Lynx. These are seldom seen except by hunters employing tracking dogs. The meat is most palatable, not unlike tender young pork.

Fox, Wolf and Coyote. These animals will be seldom seen unless extremely hungry. Their presence in the area will be revealed by their bark. Fox can be captured by a bait snare or in the Arctic, they can be captured in a baited beehive trap. Locate the trap on a high point as the fox usually travels over rather than around hills.

Bait snare, Front view
Balance pole tied to adjacent tree. Ensure that the weighted balance pole is balanced and positioned so that it will lift the victim clear of the ground.

Side view, showing trigger mechanism
Dotted line represents the fence which ensures that the animal must insert its head through the noose to obtain the bait.

A Cord to trigger mechanism
B Cord with noose

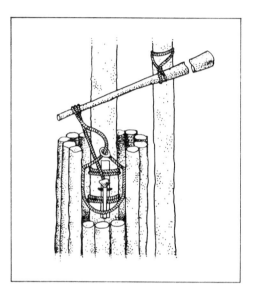

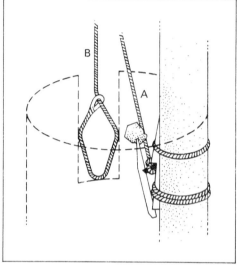

Upland Game Birds. Grouse and partridge are most often found roosting in thickets, sunning on side slopes, or feeding on the ground. Usually these birds will not fly very far when frightened and, therefore, it is better to flush them out, wait for them to land before shooting them.

If their roosting area can be found they are snared easily by using a pole with a wire noose attached to the end. Be certain and take the partridge closest to you. In this way you will not frighten the others.

Spruce grouse and the ptarmigan in the Arctic frequently remain motionless thereby seeking to avoid detection. Some may be killed by throwing sticks and rocks.

Water Fowl. Birds such as ducks, geese and coots are usually more difficult to approach than upland game. These may be shot taking into consideration the way the wind and current will take them. If geese or ducks are found during the moulting period, it may be possible to run them to the ground. Do not overlook the eggs or the very young.

Other Birds. All Canadian Birds are edible but do not waste ammunition for little gain. The Ojibway Snare will be quite effective in capuring many of these smaller birds.

Beehive Trap. Constructed from piled up rocks and stones.

Ojibway bird snare. For the bird to obtain bait it must land on the perch which is held in place by tension of the knot. Weight of the bird releases the tension on the knot and the weight on the side of the post pulls snare tight on bird's legs.

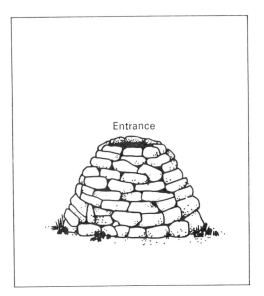

Entrance

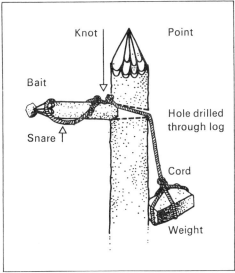

Knot   Point

Bait

Hole drilled through log

Snare

Cord

Weight

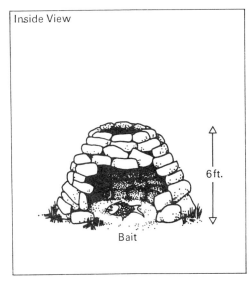

Inside View

6 ft.

Bait

Seal. The Common Jar Seal, found along most of the Arctic coastline, is an animal which the survivor may capture and from it obtain food and fuel (blubber).

During the winter the Common Jar Seal lives under the ice and maintains open breathing holes, which are usually well hidden and covered with snow. The seal is captured here by waiting without motion until it surfaces and then shooting it in the head. In the spring, the seal may be stalked as it suns itself on the ice. It will raise its head every minute or so to view the horizon. At this time the stalker should remain motionless. If white clothing is not available for camouflage, the stalker should crawl and slither up to the seal.

A method of snaring antlered game. Use a strong dry pole about 10 feet long and six inches in diameter.

Big Game

Big game will provide food for a prolonged period, but it requires a suitable gun, skill, a large expenditure of energy and some means of preserving.

Most of the large game animals are abroad at dawn and toward evening. The dawn hunt is the best for the survivor. If he becomes lost he will have all day to find his way back to camp. If he is fortunate in obtaining game he has the remaining part of the day to dress it and begin the preservation of the meat.

The Deer Family. Deer and moose are found throughout Canada's forest zone while elk and woodland caribou are most common in Western Canada.

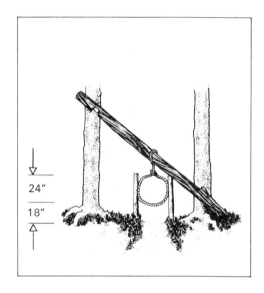

In summer, follow ridges overlooking open country but avoid showing yourself against the skyline. Look for salt-licks and wallows. Flies and ticks torment these animals during hot weather and they take refuge in wallows. This frantic splashing can be heard at considerable distance. Watch for game trails since most animals prefer to use these when travelling. In winter, the deer, elk and moose usually *"yard up"* in low lying protected areas, such as cedar swamps, willow clumps, alder swales or other thickets.

When stalking game, hunt upwind or crosswind. Avoid making a noise and stop frequently to scan the area.

If an animal starts up suddenly, remain stationary as they often return to investigate what has caused the disturbance.

Should you wound an animal, do not follow it immediately. If you attempt to follow, it may run for miles before dropping, but if you wait ten minutes, it may lie down after a short run and either bleed or stiffen up. When game is taken, bleed, clean and cool as soon as possible.

Snaring
Snares may be set on well worn paths and thus save many hours of walking. A snare made of a cable or heavy wire 24 inches in diameter and suspended about 18 inches above ground should produce good results. Make certain that the snare is well anchored.

Barren Land Caribou. Once a caribou herd is located, little trouble is experienced in shooting them particularly when migrating. Approach them low and upwind. When they are grazing in the valley, they watch the horizon.

Bears. Most bears are not dangerous unless inspired or provoked. All bears may attack if wounded so it is essential to be well armed and cautious in hunting these animals.

Fishing and Netting
Gill netting is most effective in still water near the inlet or an outlet to a stream. Nets can be constructed using the inner cords of parachute shroud lines. The floats on the top and weights on the bottom of the net keep it vertical. When the lake is covered

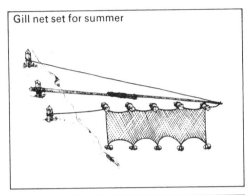
Gill net set for summer

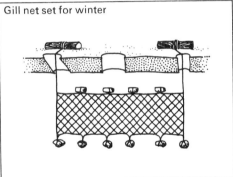
Gill net set for winter

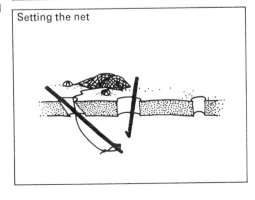
Setting the net

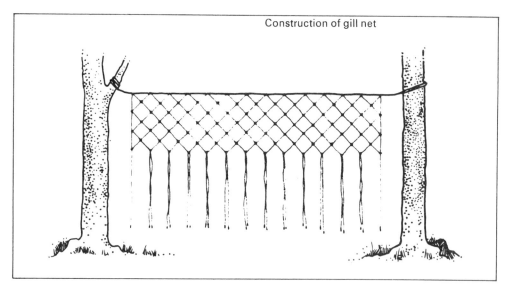

Construction of gill net

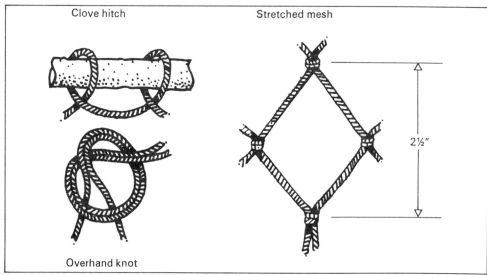

Clove hitch

Stretched mesh

2½"

Overhand knot

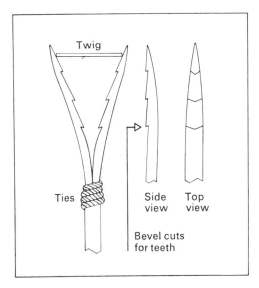

Twig

Ties

Side
view

Top
view

Bevel cuts
for teeth

pull the pole through "A" until it is set as shown. Ensure that the line is tied at both ends of the net to assist in checking and resetting.

Spearing. Clear water is a requisite for spearing. To make a spear a 1½ inch green pole is split for 18 inches. Tie at the end of the split and sharpen to a point. Cut the teeth as shown. Spread the tips apart with a thin twig. This is the trigger and when released the teeth come together. When not in use the twig must be released to retain the spring. This makes an excellent spear. Along the Arctic coast, the arctic char can be attracted within spear range by bobbing a shiny object up and down.

with ice the fish stay in a deeper area. A mesh of two and one-half inches is a good standard size.

Winter setting of the net necessitates the cutting of three holes in the ice on a lake. Make certain the net is several inches below the ice to prevent it from freezing. By using a pole slightly longer than the distance between the holes attach a line to one end. Starting at Hole "A", float the pole to "B", to "C" and remove from the water at "C". Attach the net to the end of the line and

Camp Fires

Fire-Making

You will need fire for warmth, for keeping dry, for signalling, for cooking, for purifying water by boiling.

Don't build your fires too large. Small fires require less fuel and are easier to control; and their heat can be concentrated. In cold weather small fires arranged in a circle around an individual are much more effective than one large fire.

Prepare the location of your fire carefully. Clear away leaves, twigs, moss and dry grass, so that you don't start a grass or forest fire. If the ground is dry, scrape down to bare dirt. If the fire must be built on ice, snow or wet ground, build a platform of logs or flat stones.

Outdoor Fires

Obtain dry twigs and dead limbs. Set the twigs up teepee-like over tinder paper, dry leaves, pine needles or shavings. Ignite the tinder and wait until the blaze is well started before adding larger and harder wood. For fuel, use dry standing dead wood and dry dead branches. Dead wood is easy to split and break — pound it on a rock. In treeless areas, you can find natural fuels such as dry grass which you can twist into bunches. When a sufficient quantity of fuel is obtained, start the kindling and gradually add the larger fuel.

Save matches by using a candle, if you have one or use a shave stick or small faggot of thin dry twigs, tied loosely. If matches or a lighter are not available prepare very dry powdered wood, finely shredded dry-bark, lint from cloth, twine or fuzzy material scraped from plants; fine bird feathers or nests. These may be ignited by striking a piece of flint on steel, the use of burning glass (the convex lens on a flashlight) or by friction.

1 Light your fire with a candle—
note proper way to lay fire.

3 Lighting a fire with a flint and steel.

2, 4 Bow and drill method of firemaking.

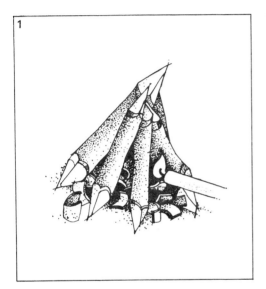

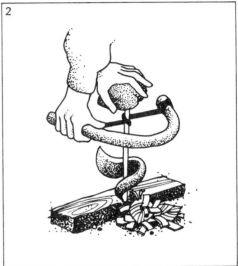

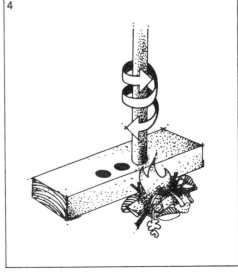

Types of Fires

A successful fire depends on how you arrange the wood. Cooking fires can be arranged in several different ways, according to the type of food available and the method of cooking that is chosen. The cooking part of a fire is the bed of glowing embers that is left after the flames have died down. Four basic types are discussed here, but many other arrangements and variations are possible.

Teepee Fire

The teepee arrangement is the simplest and most usual way of building a fire. It is easy to build and light, burns quickly, and can be used for most cooking arrangements. Several other types of fires and cooking arrangements are simply elaborations added to a basic teepee fire.

Star Fire

This arrangement is particularly appropriate for frying. Begin with a small teepee fire and arrange three or four logs around it with one end in the fire and the rest of the logs pointing away. The ends of the logs support the pan over the fire in the centre. As the log ends burn down keep pushing the logs into the embers.

Log Cabin Fire

This arrangement makes a good roasting or boiling fire. Again, start with a small central teepee fire and add larger logs around the outside in a square, "log-cabin" pattern. As the logs burn away, collapse the remains into the central fire and add new logs around the outside.

Trapper Fire

The trapper fire makes a good boiling or stewing fire. Start by building a small teepee fire, and add a large, green log or stones on either side, so the fire is burning in the hollow between their ends. The other ends of the logs should be closer together, and if there is a wind blowing the wider end of the trench should be upwind. As embers form, push them toward the narrow end of the trench, and place the cooking pots over them.

1 Arrangement of teepee fire

2 Star Fire

3 Log Cabin Fire

4 Trapper Fire

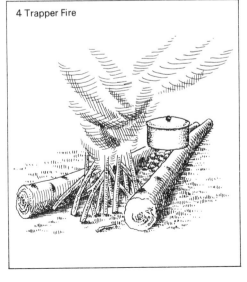

5 *Teepee fire* for use in teepee
quick meals or roasting

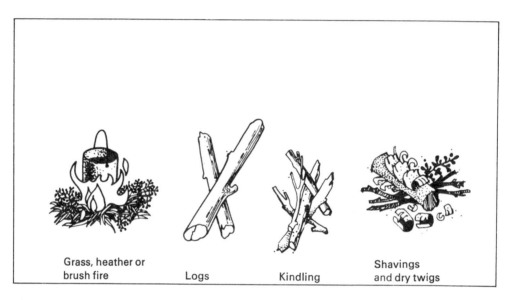

Grass, heather or
brush fire

Logs

Kindling

Shavings
and dry twigs

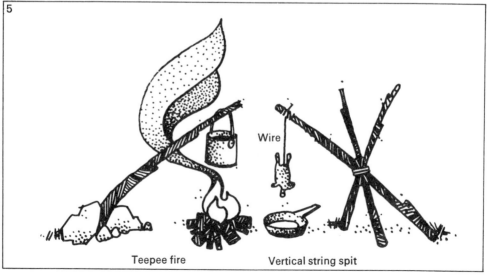

Wire

Teepee fire

Vertical string spit

A simple method of suspending the pot over the fire.

Broiling and barbecuing or roasting.
Use a weight on the butt of the pole if necessary. The pole can be rotated to baste all sides of the meat.

Meat should be held to the side of hot coals not over them. Avoid smoke and flame. Use a receptacle to catch drippings.

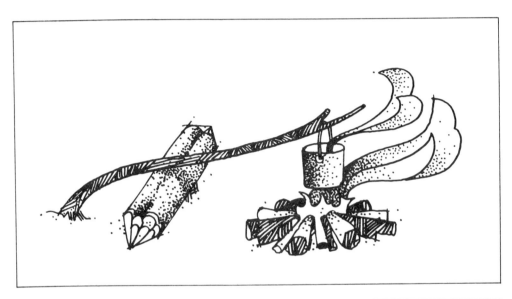

Universal sapling pot hook
Can be hung from string, wire or pole

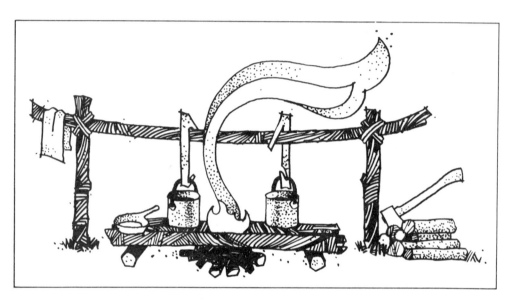

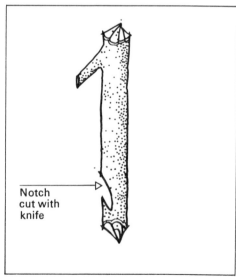

Notch
cut with
knife

Cooking of Meat and Fish

Boiling. This is the best method of preparing meat for human consumption. It is easy and it requires less fuel than other methods.

If you drink the resultant broth as well, you get the full food value. A small quantity will feed a number of people and there will be no waste. In order to ensure that all meat is properly done, have the chunks of equal size.

Frying and Broiling. These can be done if utensils are available and if there is sufficient food available. A certain amount of the food value is wasted, and above the tree line where you may have only a limited quantity of fuel, you may waste it.

Barbecuing or Roasting. This is an easy method and often produces the tastiest results, though it causes the most waste. Clean the fish or small animal and spike it on the end of a green stick elevated beside a hot fire which produces as little smoke and flame as possible. If necessary turn the meat occasionally to assure it is thoroughly cooked. A great quantity of nutritious juice is lost by this method and there is considerable shrinkage. However, this can be partially counteracted by either placing the meat very close to the fire at first to form a hard crust on the outside which will contain the juices, or having the meat suspended at one end of the fire with a shallow plate underneath to catch the drippings.

Protection of Food from Animals

Surplus food and supplies should be cached. There are numerous methods of doing this. The best is to suspend the meat by rope, away from trees or uprights.

The main threat to your cache is animals, from the bear to the mouse. The cache should be high enough to prevent attack from the ground, ten to fifteen feet, and far enough out from the uprights that climbing and springing animals will have difficulty reaching it. Squirrels and Canada Jays are the nuisances. Food can be covered to ward off the meat-hungry birds, but from the preservation point of view, it is advisable to have the cover fit loosely so that air can circulate around it.

Single pole cache

Wire suspension cache

Shelters

People stranded in the north and facing the possibility of a long wait will probably want to construct shelters such as those shown on the following pages; these shelters will be of greater or lesser complexity depending on the time and materials available, and the needs of the people involved.

Do not forget, however, that in an emergency, shelter is anything that keeps the elements at bay. It is not necessary to construct an elaborate shelter if something simple will do. There are many instances where lack of time, shortage of materials, or other more pressing problems make it undesirable to devote your limited energy to constructing a large and elaborate shelter.

Shelters of First Priority

Trees. Basic shelter can frequently be found under trees, particularly evergreens such as cedar, spruce or balsam that have large, spreading lower branches. Snow can be heaped up around the lower branches of these trees to form a protected hollow.

Snow. With its large proportion of air spaces, snow is a natural insulator. Burrowing into a snow bank or covering yourself with loose snow will provide a basic, insulated sleeping space on the trail or in situations where there is no time to build anything else. This is particuarly the case during sudden blizzards or snow squalls.

Your Plane or Vehicle. Even if your aircraft or other conveyance is damaged to the point where it is not usable for shelter, do not overlook materials that may be scavenged from it, such as plastic or metal sheeting, floorboards, carpet, insulation, or seat coverings.

Shelters in Bush Areas

The following notes are adopted from *"Down But Not Out"*, published by Information Canada.

When it is necessary to spend a night on the trail or in an emergency (especially involving injuries to members of the party) it may be an advantage to build a shelter. The most common and practical is the "Lean-To".

The Lean-To

A pole framework is covered with a thatching of evergreen boughs or rushes. When constructing the lean-to, find two trees seven to nine feet apart with fairly level, firm ground between them. The distance between the trees will be the length of the opening of the lean-to although it is possible to incorporate variations. The number of people requiring shelter should determine the size. When constructed for one man it should be made long enough for him to sleep across the open mouth of the shelter, whereas for more than one it should be planned for them to sleep lengthwise. One or both ends of the ridge pole may be supported by a pole tripod if a second tree is not available. This leaves the builder a wider choice of sites. It should be remembered that the steeper the slope angle of the roof the better it will shed rain and reflect heat from the fire. A 45 degree slope angle is generally considered a suitable compromise between available interior space and rain shedding effectiveness.

Once the framework has been constructed, proceed with the covering. Spruce boughs make an excellent natural covering, although the branches of any coniferous and of many deciduous trees will do. They are placed on the lean-to in the same manner as shingles on a roof, the first row at the bottom and the last row at the top. The brush ends of the boughs are placed down, overlapping the butt ends of the previous row. This method of thatching ensures that rain will be shed more readily. Continue to lay rows of boughs in this fashion until the top of the lean-to is covered. Repeat the thatching procedure until the entire roof is covered to a depth of at least six inches. The triangular sides are filled in with large boughs set butt end up as in thatching.

Para-Teepee

This is a simply erected teepee. Cut three poles approximately twelve feet in length. Tie these with rope or strips of skins or bark about eight inches from one end and set up as a tripod. Place extra poles about the tripod

Fabric Lean-to. When made with 14 segments of parachute will shelter 6 men. Use any fabric material such as airplane insulation panels or wing covers.

Para-Teepee. Note Shroud-lines cut off and tied into peg-loops. The only fabric shelter in which an open fire can be built.

Slab Lean-to. Made of rotten log casings. Can be made without tools. Lay casings in Spanish tile manner.

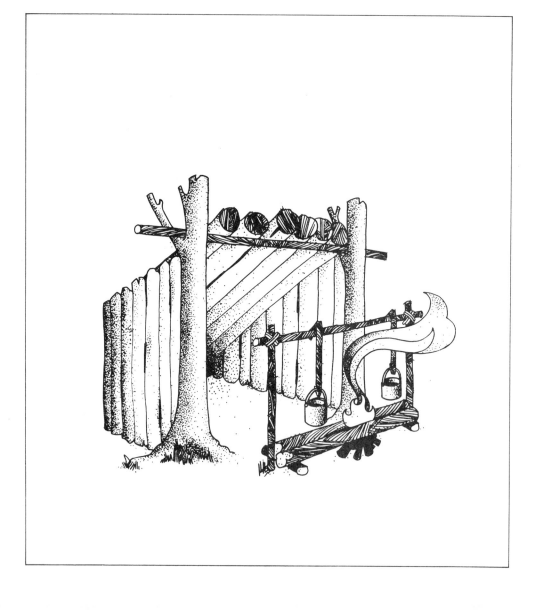

1 One-Pole Set 10 Segment Para-Teepee

2 Floor Plan of Para-Teepee showing position of sleeping bags and fire.

3 *Tarp-Cabin.* Construct the four walls in log-cabin fashion and then build the framework of light poles.

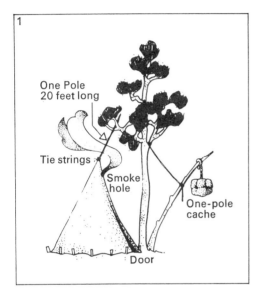

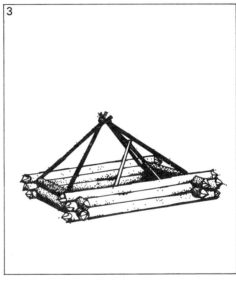

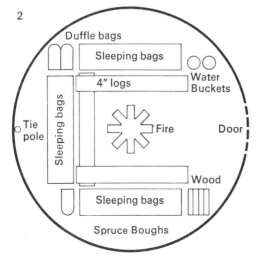

and lace together at the top. These may be covered with canvas or spruce boughs. Arrange the boughs in rows starting at the bottom and ending at the top. The front openings of all shelters should be kept crosswind. A fire is usually built in front of the opening.

Tarp-Cabin

This shelter requires a considerable amount of work and when completed will have a degree of permanency that other previously mentioned shelters do not have. In building the cabin, particular attention should be paid to the choice of location, as the cabin is not portable. Choose an area close to a water supply, yet not in a valley. The ridges offer much more comfortable living conditions, freedom from insects, flooding, etc. The area chosen should also offer an abundant supply of long straight logs, four to eight inches in diameter. Build four walls log cabin fashion to a height of about three feet and then build a framework of light poles to support a covering of parachute material or canvas.

Canvas. From this stage it is a simple matter to place this material over the framework to form a finished shelter. It is preferable to employ a double layer of fabric with an air space between to improve the insulating and water shedding qualities of the roof.

Shelters in the Arctic

Tools. The combination snow saw-knife or a snow knife is almost essential to survival north of the tree line. With it snow blocks can be cut to build a shelter while on the trail or if lost.

Material. The snow from which the snow house is buit should be in a firmly packed and frozen form with several characteristics not often encountered south of the tree line. The snow should be solid enough that a cubic foot block will support the weight of a man, yet it can be cut, sawed, or split with ease. Only a small percentage of snow is suitable for snow house building. First search for an area where snow-drifts are deep enough to permit cutting snow blocks from a vertical face. This will require a depth of nearly two feet. The snow should be firm enough to support your weight with only a slight marking by foot prints. Probe into the snow with your saw-knife or a long sturdy stick. Try to find a place where the resistance to the probe indicates an even firm structure, free of harder or softer layers. When you find a spot, probe around to ascertain whether enough good snow is available.

It is well worth hunting for an hour to find proper snow as you will save the time during snow house building. If snow of sufficient depth to cut vertical blocks cannot be found, it will be necessary to cut them from the flat surface of snow. This is time consuming and requires a much larger area of snow,

The snow blocks are stood on each side of the trench.

When the trench is completed a notch is cut along each side to provide non-slip support for the snow block roof. A triangular block is placed at one end of the trench as a support for the first snow block of the roof.

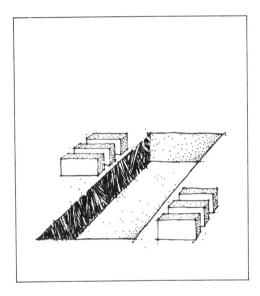

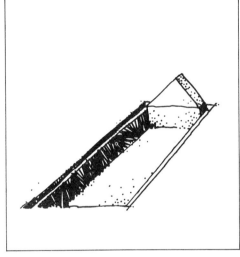

and the snow house will have to be built higher, because it cannot be dug into the drift.

The Fighter Trench

If time does not permit building an igloo, a fighter trench can be built easily and quickly with minimum work for the result achieved. This is simply a trench dug in the snow and covered by blocks to form a shelter.

If a large drift of snow at least three feet deep is available, the shelter can be made by cutting large vertical blocks from a trench wider than the sleeping bag and long enough to accommodate the one or two builders. The snow blocks are stood on each side of the trench.

When the trench is completed a notch is cut along each side to provide non-slip support for the snow block roof. A triangular block is placed at one end of the trench as a support for the first snow block of the roof.

The first roofing snow block is cut narrower than the others, in order that the succeeding blocks will overlap, each supporting the next. The remainder of the roof blocks are placed in a similar manner.

The first roofing snow block A, is cut narrower than the others, in order that the succeeding blocks will overlap, each supporting the next.

The remainder of the roof blocks are placed in a similar manner.

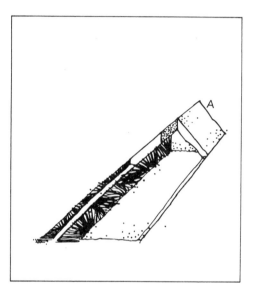

In a two man trench an entrance door is placed halfway down the trench, opening into a roofed-over square pit which allows room for cooking and removing clothing before entering the sleeping bag. Be sure to cut a ventilating hole in the roof and have a good snow block handy to close the entrance at night.

If no deep snow drifts can be found, a trench style shelter can be erected by building a wall of blocks enclosing the shelter area. This wall is then roofed over with large slabs which are hollowed slightly on the inside, after erection to form an arch.

The fighter trench while a good emergency shelter is too cramped to permit much movement without dislodging the frost on your clothing and sleeping bag, and in time you will become damp without a good means of drying out. This is why you should begin your igloo as soon as possible.

The Igloo

The word *"igloo"* is of Eskimo origin. In that language it is a general word for "house" or "shelter". It will be used to mean the domed snow house, similar to that used by some Eskimo groups particularly in the central Arctic.

Everyone who travels on land in the Arctic or the barren lands in winter should be able to build a snow house. This skill could easily mean the difference between life or death if an accident or sudden blizzard conditions make unexpected delays necessary.

In a two man trench an entrance door is placed halfway down the trench, opening into a roofed-over square pit which allows room for cooking and removing clothing before entering the sleeping bag.

Be sure to cut a ventilating hole in the roof and have a good snow block handy to close the entrance at night.

Ground plan of igloo
A Sleeping platform
B Storage platforms
C Passage through door

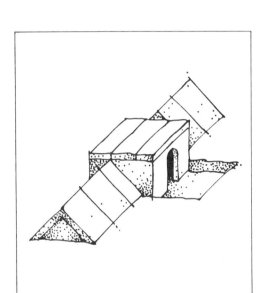

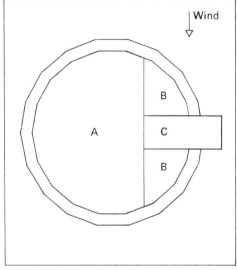

The Eskimo igloo is the ideal winter shelter in the Arctic. It is solid, sound-proof and wind-resistant, and is large enough for comfort. There are a few building techniques which must be mastered but none of these are particularly difficult. Once the method is learned, the igloo will amost invariably be the shelter used in an emergency.

When you have found a good snow-drift, lay out the floor plan. The Eskimo does this by eye, but he usually has had a lot of practice. Draw a circle centered on snow, firm enough to support a person and at least twenty inches deep with the approximate diameter as follows:

One man	8 feet
Two men	9 feet
Three men	10 feet
Four men	12 feet
Five men	13 feet

Now, begin to lay in a supply of snow blocks. Cut them from the face of a trench, laid out as shown, and to the depth of at least twenty inches. Begin cutting blocks by digging out a clear vertical face at A-B, with a width of about 46 inches and a depth of about 20 inches. Smaller blocks are not much easier to cut, and igloo construction is slower and more difficult with them.

Cross section of igloo
A 1 Foot above level of snow
B 6 Inches above level of snow
C Door passage
D Snow

Using a snow saw-knife saw along the ends of the block. Cut the blocks about 6" thick and break off at the bottom. Cut about a dozen blocks before starting to build.

Dimensions of blocks about 36 inches long, 18 inches wide and 6 inches thick.

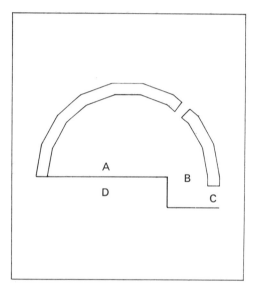

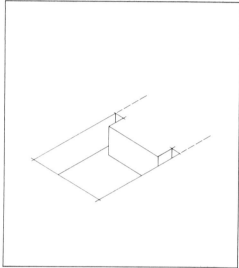

With your snow saw-knife, cut a slot at each end of the block, about two inches wide and the full depth of the block.

Next, score a groove parallel to the face, marking off a block about six inches thick.

If you have a snow saw-knife, saw along this mark, breaking off the block with a firm jab in the centre. If you are using a snow knife, deepen the groove by running the point back and forth, then three or four gentle stabs and a firm central stroke will break it off.

Lift the snow block to one side and begin another. When you have about a dozen cut, then you may begin to build.

When the first row reaches the snow block trench, a snow block is replaced in it to permit the wall to be taken across it. Note the slope of the first row of blocks. All end joints are fitted with faces radial to the igloo centre, or you are heading for trouble.

When the first row is finished, begin the spiral which will end at the key block. If you are right handed, cut away any three blocks diagonally, sloping down from left to right. If you are left handed cut the slope the other way.

First tier completed, showing 3 blocks cut to form inclined plane.

When the first row is finished, begin the spiral which will end at the key block. If you are right handed, cut away any three blocks diagonally, sloping down from left to right. If you are left handed cut the slope the other way.

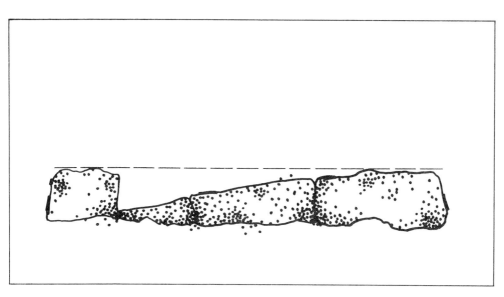

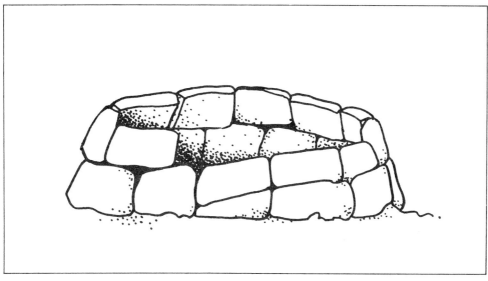

The block must bear only at areas A, B and C. It should not bear at D or E or it will pivot and slip.

When the third row is under construction, the slope will be great enough to make careful fitting essential.

Each block bears on the same three positions only.

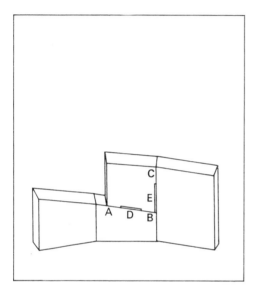

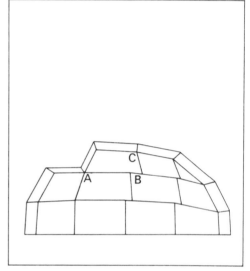

Now fit the next block, leaning it inward so that its inner face is roughly a tangent to the dome. Even at this early stage, the block might fall in, except that it is supported by the face of the notch and the top of the previous blocks.

The block must bear only at areas A, B and C. It should not bear at D or E or it will pivot and slip. All blocks from this point on, until the key block, are set in this manner.

Continue cutting blocks from within the the igloo circle, fitting them as you go. Don't use blocks less than two feet long or eighteen inches wide if you can help it. Lay small blocks aside for later use in snow bench and doorway building. The slope of the block, which of course governs the shape of the igloo, is estimated by eye. The block is raised into place and the joints are trimmed until the block settles into position.

When the third row is under construction, the slope will be great enough to make careful fitting essential. Each block bears on the same three positions only. The remainder

When you run out of block snow inside the igloo, cautiously cut a small door as far down the wall as you can, tunnelling underneath to make enough space for the outside workers to push in more building blocks.

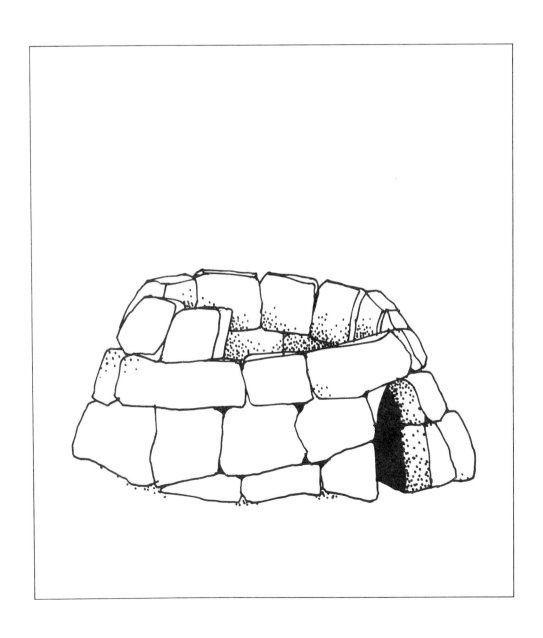

When the remaining hole in the roof is small
enough to permit doing so, a key block is fitted.
After what you have been doing, this is easy.

The edges of the hole should be bevelled at
about 15 degrees from the vertical.

Try to keep the curve of the walls symmetrical and avoid a pointed igloo, because the high ceiling will allow the heat to be above the sleeping bench.

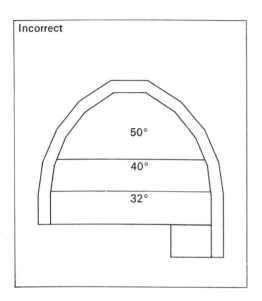

Incorrect

50°
40°
32°

Correct

50°
40°

of the joint can gape wide, or almost touch, but these three faces must carry the load to jam in the block.

The tendency to rotate inward about A-B is resisted by pressure between the upper third of the faces of the new block and the previous block at C. This face must be radial to the igloo centre, or the previous block may be displaced.

When fitting snow blocks on the A-B-C method described, the block should be lifted into position and the joint fitted roughly, with the faces in contact and the block supported by the left hand. If the snow saw-knife is run between the new block and the previous one to make them fit, then a slight

undercut on the under face at the end nearest the previous block will leave the joint supported at A and C only. A firm tap downward at C as shown by the arrow will drive the block into final position, seating at A, B and C, when it need no longer be supported.

Carry on building, block by block. You will find that the increasing slope of the igloo wall will of course increase the tendency for the block to fall in, but this is compensated by the increasing angle between the A-B axis of the successive blocks as the diameter of the opening decreases. Building

Across the floor, about one third of the way back from the door, build a snow wall about 20 inches high to conserve warmth. This will form the front of your sleeping shelf, which will raise you into the warm air trapped above the door.

Plan of Igloo showing position of sleeping shelf, door and snow block, outside door.

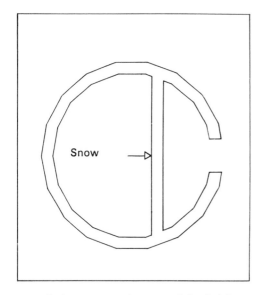

Snow

Sleeping shelf

Door

block

actually becomes easier toward the finish, as the blocks will jam firmly into place.

When you run out of block snow inside the igloo, cautiously cut a small door as far down the wall as you can, tunnelling underneath to make enough space for the outside workers to push in more building blocks.

Try to keep the curve of the walls symmetrical and avoid a pointed igloo, because the high ceiling would reach the limiting warmth before the sleeping bench gets it share of heat.

It is surprising how flat an arch can be built using the spiral technique. The last few

blocks will be almost horizontal, but if you remember the A-B-C fit, they won't fall.

When the remaining hole in the roof is small enough to permit doing so, a key block is fitted. After what you have been doing, this is easy. The edges of the hole should be bevelled at about 15 degrees fron the vertical. The hole should be longer than it is wide, to permit passing the key block up through, then juggling it into position. This is tricky, but not as difficult as it may appear. By judicious use of your snow knife, cut away the block, letting it settle slowly into position. You have built your igloo!

Floor plan of igloo showing position of sleeping bags, stove and equipment.

Shove all the loose snow in the igloo behind the wall to form the shelf. Break up lumps and blocks to soften the bench and to provide better insulation. Level the bench top carefully.

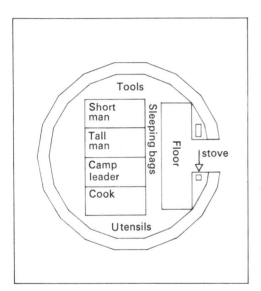

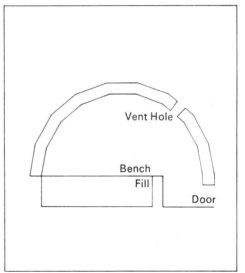

Making the Igloo Habitable

Across the floor, about one third of the way back from the door, build a snow wall about 20 inches high to conserve warmth. This will form the front of your sleeping shelf, which will raise you into the warm air trapped above the door.

Shove all the loose snow in the igloo behind the wall to form the shelf. Break up lumps and blocks to soften the bench and to pro- vide better insulation. Level the bench top carefully. At each side of the door leave or erect little benches allowing about 20 inches of leg room between the sleeping shelf and bench.

This is the kitchen and heating area. It must be reasonably close to the bench to permit the cook and lamp tender to reach it without rising from the sleeping bench on which he is sitting. Chink the dome of the igloo care- fully with powder snow, which when packed firmly into the open seams will soon harden and stop loss of warm air from the igloo.

If you plan a short stay, chink only the outer seams, but for a better job do both inside and outside joints. You may throw loose powdery snow on top of the igloo to act as chinking, but not so much as to add to the weight of the roof. You may bank the bottom row of blocks to prevent wind driven snow from causing erosion.

Fitting the key block.
Pass the key block up through the hole and using your snow knife cut the block to fit into the opening.

Throw powdery snow on the top of the igloo to close up the openings between blocks, and bank around the base to prevent erosin. A ventilating hole is a must if a fire of any nature is being used for cooking or heating.

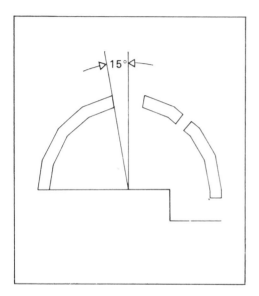

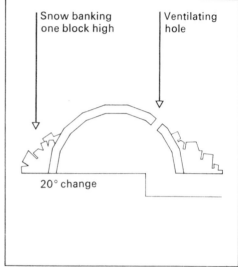

If a high wind is blowing, the drifting snow can erode the wall of the igloo very rapidly. A snow wall should be erected to act as a wind-break, and any broken blocks can be piled against the windward wall to protect it from the cutting effect of the drift.

Now, with the igloo chinked, the door cut in and the sleeping bench completed, all you need to do before moving in is to clear out all loose snow. The bench is first covered with caribou skins (or other insulation) and the sleeping bags are then unrolled and placed, heads to the entrance, side by side. All snow and frost must be removed from hides, bedding, and clothing before they are placed on the sleeping bench.

Drying racks made by forcing sticks into the walls, above the heat sources will serve the following purposes:

a) Drying of clothing from which all snow, ice, and frost have first been scraped. Never melt snow on garments, always scrape it off.
b) Thawing of frozen rations which do not need cooking. This requires quite a long time.
c) Protection of the igloo wall and roof from melting.

The Eskimo fat burning lamp, or *Koolik,* has provided heat for comfort and cooking for thousands of years, giving a quiet pleasant light and warmth to the native home.

Improvise a fat lamp out of a ration can, using heavy cotton, linen cloth as a wick. Oil or fat may be used as fuel.

Pots can be suspended from pegs driven firmly into the walls above the fat lamp *koolik* or the primus stove *koodlik.*

Koolik. The Eskimo fat burning lamp, or koolik, has provided heat for comfort and cooking for thousands of years, giving a quiet and pleasant light and warmth to the native home. Properly tended it does not smoke or smell, and it can be controlled to give more or less heat on demand. It is carved laboriously from soap-stone in the form of a shallow pan of half-moon shape. The straight edge of the lamp are bevelled to support the wick, made of Arctic cotton or moss.

Seal oil or caribou fat is used as fuel. To avoid its melting into the snow shelf and to keep it warm enough to render fat, it is supported on short sticks driven into the shelf.

Some Rules for Living in an Igloo
Persons entering the igloo for a stay of longer than an hour or so, after removing mukluks and snow from garments, should get up on the sleeping bench, out of the way.

The cook, usually at the right-hand bench, has the primus stove, under which is a piece of cardboard from a ration box to prevent it from melting into the shelf and tipping. He may also have a *koolik,* if fat is available, for slow cooking.

One person should be responsible for adequate ventilation — keeping the vent holes in the dome and door open enough to avoid risk without freezing the occupants. *Carbon Monoxide is insidious and dangerous.*

During the day the door is left open. At night it is closed by a snow block which should be chinked and a ventilating hole three inches to six inches in diameter bored through the upper part. The more fumes being generated, the larger must be the aperture. Don't wait until the lamp won't burn properly and you begin to feel groggy before letting in air. It is dangerous, and isn't necessary. If the roof hole does not draw properly because of wind, a snow chimney can be made by setting a perforated block over the hole.

Now that you are in residence, the igloo will warm up rapidly. If the inner walls start to glaze with ice, and drip, you are overheating. Take corrective action before icing develops; cut down the heat if you must.

Frying, baking or broiling have no place in igloo living. Boiling and stewing are easier and prove very satisfactory. Canned goods may be heated in the can by bringing them unopened to a boil in a pot of water which completely covers them. Use the pressure cooker or a tightly covered pot to avoid steam. Never place an unopened can over direct heat!

Two good meals a day, breakfast and the main meal in the evening, avoid loss of the working day. A snack at noon will not bring activity to a halt for more than an hour or so. Body heat is derived from food intake, so eat all your ration and supplement with fish whenever possible. Eat fats rather than burn them if the supply is low. A diet of meat is good for you. Vilhjalmur Stefansson lived for a full year on meat alone to prove this point. If you are forced to live solely on the products of the chase, you must eat flesh, fat, liver and every edible part, to ensure that you don't suffer from dietetic deficiencies.

You can improvise a fat lamp out of any flat pan, such as a ration can. If you have fat to burn, all that is required is a piece of heavy cotton, linen cloth, or absorbent cotton for a wick and a sloping ramp to support it. You can burn lubricating oil in a fat lamp, but the flame will smoke more readily and the wick will have to be trimmed more carefully to keep the flame below the smoking point. When the level of the oil drops, the flame may follow it down the wick, causing further smoking. A simple damper, made of the tin foil from a gum wrapper or a piece of sheet metal, will prevent this, and will permit closer control of the flame. A few drops of aircraft fuel used with caution will aid in

lighting the wick. Never try to burn a volatile
fuel in the *koolik* – you would be far
too successful, and you might find yourself
in trouble.

The left-hand men remain on the bench,
assist in cooking and maintaining their
koolik. If this lamp is burning animal fat, it
requires only moderate attention. Lubricating
oil is not so easily used, as the flame smokes
easily and the wick needs more frequent
attention.

A little animal fat dissolved in the lubricating
oil makes a big improvement in the flame.
If the group finds the igloo cluttered with
odds and ends not needed at the moment,
a miniature igloo can be built against the
outside wall, and a doorway out through to
form a cache. Keep the entrance low to
avoid loss of heat.

Equipment

Always stick your axe in a log or tree. Never lay it on the ground or snow.

Always chop against a log or block. It saves the axe and perhaps your foot! Axes are more dangerous than Grizzlies.

Care and Use of Equipment and Clothing

In the battle of man against nature, the odds greatly favor the person who is able to utilize available equipment to the full and knows how to care for it.

It has been found that some persons have failed to survive, even under reasonably good conditions, not from lack of equipment but from failure to care for it and use it to the best advantage. Here are some suggestions for the proper care and use of the various pieces of equipment found in survival kits usually carried on the trail, together with some suggestions for the fabrication of further survival aid.

Axe

This is one of the most important pieces of survival equipment, and also one of the most abused. Properly used it can simplify your survival problem, but misused, it can become a means of crippling yourself to such an extent that survival becomes impossible.

If your axe does not have a sheath, make one from any suitable material available, and keep the axe in its sheath until it is required for use. Before using, make the following checks:

a) Check the head for tightness of the handle. If it is loose, either drive the wedge further home or make a new wedge using hardwood. Soaking the head is another method but it is not recommended for winter time, as ice may form on the handle and inside the head, allowing the head to slide off and cause possible injury. To drive the handle further into the head, strike the end of the handle, not the head of the axe.

b) Check for sharpness. A dull axe can be dangerous for two reasons. First it will not bite properly and will tend to glance off the wood being cut. Secondly, when blunt it is necessary to use more force, which usually means a sacrifice of control.

c) Check that the handle is not cracked or split. A serious cut or sliver might be received.

When carrying an axe, be sure that the sharp edge is held away from the body. In the event of a fall, there will then be less chance of injury.

When felling a tree, these procedures should be followed:

a) Before beginning, clear the tree of lower limbs, and remove the underbrush from around the bottom of the tree. This is to ensure that the axe is not deflected during the swing.

b) Check your distance from the tree to avoid underreaching or overreaching. Overreaching can result in breaking the axe handle: underreaching in a cut foot.

c) Take up a comfortable stance, making sure that both feet are firmly set.

d) The first cut should be made on the side of the tree facing the direction of the desired fall, often decided by the "lean" of the tree. This cut should be not more than half-way through the tree. The back cut should be commenced slightly above and opposite the first cut.

e) It is safest to cut the tree off not over a foot above the ground. Always keep the axe handle low, i.e., parallel to the ground where the blade strikes the cut. When using short handled axes or hand axes bend carefully at the hips or kneel on one knee.

When splitting wood, do not lay the piece to be split on the ground, but support it as illustrated. This not only prevents the axe from chopping into the ground and becoming blunted, but may also prevent injury to legs or feet.

When finished with the axe, clean the head carefully, replace the sheath, and store in an upright position. It is permissible to store by sticking it in a dry stump, but green wood should never be used for this purpose.

Knife

As with the axe, the knife should be kept sharp and carried in a stout sheath. Return it to the sheath immediately after use. Always position the sheath on your belt towards the back of the hip, since with the knife in a forward position it is possible that a fall could drive the knife into the groin. Guard against loss by attaching a cord from the handle of the knife to your belt or belt loop. Never throw your knife. It is ineffective when so misused and it will probably be damaged or lost.

Firearms

Rules for the proper care of your firearms are as follows:

a) In cold weather, store your firearms in a sheltered cold spot. Avoid moving between the warm shelter and cold outdoors as eventually, because of the condensation of moisture on the metal parts, the protective blueing will break down and allow the metal to rust. Also remove grease and oil from the weapon and replace them with non-freezing oil or graphite. If neither is available, the moving parts can be rubbed with a pencil or the gun can be used without lubrication.

b) Keep the barrel clean at all times. A plugged barrel may cause a firearm to explode, with serious injury to the user.

c) Always prove your weapon when storing it or picking it up. "Empty" guns have caused many fatalities.

d) Store guns and ammunition in a safe dry place.

Snow Saw-Knife

In the Arctic, the snow saw-knife is one of the most useful tools in your possession. Guard against loss by sticking it upright in the snow when not in use. At night take it into the shelter with you, because it may be necessary to cut your way out in the morning. Avoid chopping ice or frozen meat with it; under extremely cold conditions this can chip or shatter the blade.

Ice Chisel

As with all edged tools, it should be kept sharp. When using the ice chisel make a cord loop, attach it to the end of the handle and loop it over your wrist. This will guard against loss when the chisel breaks through the ice.

Make a drying frame for your clothes. Never place clothing nearer to the fire than you can comfortably hold your hand. Dry the lining separately if your clothes get wet.

Sleeping Bag or Bedding

In summer, keep your sleeping bag or bedding dry, air it when weather conditions permit, and shake it daily. Roll up lightly when not in use.

In winter, keep it free of snow. Open it completely every morning and gently beat off any frost which may have formed during the night. Roll the bag or bedding up lightly and cover to protect it from the snow when not in use. Air your bedding as often as weather will permit and shake the sleeping bag gently to restore resiliency to the feathers. If using wood fires for heat, guard against spark damage. If a hole should occur in your bag, repair it immediately, possibly by using part of a skin. Considerable loss of insulation could result if a hole is not repaired when first noticed.

Clothing

It is even more important to keep your clothing clean and in good repair while travelling or during survival than it is during your everyday life in the settlement. Good hygiene is of course essential and the clothes on your back will probably be the only ones you have until you return or are picked up.

Use your clothing wisely, making every effort to keep them clean and dry at all times.

If your clothes become wet, dry them as soon as possible. Socks and mitts particularly should be kept dry. These will usually get damp during a day's wearing. Unless too damp they can be dried quite effectively by placing them in your sleeping bag before retiring and leaving them there for the night. If a hole is worn in a sock, turn the sock over to prevent a blister on the heel.

In winter it is best to dress lightly when exerting yourself, and have extra clothing handy to put on when sitting around idle. When working in a parka, it is wise to drop the hood and allow the warm air around your body to escape. The hood can be raised again when work is completed.

In the Arctic, damp clothing can be left to freeze and the moisture beaten out of it when frozen. In the bush, clothing may be dried by the fire. Take the following precautions:

a) Never place clothing nearer to the fire than you can comfortably hold your hand.
b) Never leave clothing by an untended fire.
c) When drying leather foot-wear, turn it and work the leather periodically to keep it pliable. When almost completely dry, apply a good coating of dubbin or fat, working the grease well into the seams and pores of the leather. Do not heat mukluks or leather.

Miscellaneous Equipment

Your camp will contain many small items which can easily become lost if not looked after. The following rules apply to such pieces of gear which are not usually carried on the person but are used by everyone in the party.

a) Have a designated place for the equipment, and return it after use. Have this location well marked, and make everyone in the party aware of its existence.
b) Never lay equipment down on snow, spruce boughs, or ground. Put it in your pocket or hang it in a conspicuous place.
c) Place your equipment in an accessible place, so that you can reach such items as your signal flares at a moment's notice.
d) Small items, such as the compass and match container, should be tied to the person to avoid loss while travelling.

Other General Rules

Do not cut rope or twine unless absolutely necessary, as you may need it later in its original length.

Make sure your cooking is done on level solid ground to guard against tipping. Fill your primus stove, lantern, etc., away from your shelter, and over some utensil that will catch spills, thus reducing waste and eliminating the fire hazard.

Make a habit of tying knots which can easily be undone, such as the bowline, clove hitch (see section on Knots), particularly in cold weather.

Improvisations

If the Eskimos and Indians had accepted defeat because equipment was not available, these representative races would not be found upon this planet. There are many things which must be improvised if you find yourself in a downed plane or lost in your travels in the Arctic until rescue comes.

As much material as possible should be taken from the aircraft if you are leaving it. These materials along with those provided by nature will not only assist you in surviving but also enable you to live comfortably.

A piece of wood 3" in diameter and about 20 inches in length may be split into a plank and fabricated into a snow knife or saw. Eating utensils may be formed out of wood, bone or even rock. Any material which is waterproof or animal skins may be used to hold water. The water may be heated by dropping hot stones into the container. A stretcher may be made by passing two long poles through the sleeves of a coat and then buttoning the main body over the poles.

While it is true energy should be conserved it is equally important that the mind must be kept busy. Experiment with new ideas and new principles. Although emergency packs are most helpful it is of equal importance to know how to use all the equipment along with what nature has provided.

Improvised Equipment

The following improvisations of useful equipment have been developed in the past:
a) Needles from bone or metal parts;
b) Fish lures from various combinations of wood, metal and brightly coloured cloth;
c) Snow knives from wood, metal or bone;
d) Water bottles from bark, the internal organs and skins of animals;
e) Good whisk broom from wings of birds;
f) Eating utensils from bone, wood or metal;
g) Eye snow shields from wood or from cloth;
h) The bow drill principle can be used for drilling holes in objects;
i) A parachute may be used for covering a pole shelter, ground sheets, and the cords used for lacing.

Knots

A few of the various knots will be of value
to a person attempting to survive in the
North. There are four basic requirements for
knots:

1 They must be easy to tie and untie.
2 They can be tied if necessary in the mid-
dle of a length of rope.
3 They can be tied when the rope is under
tension.
4 They can be tied in such a fashion that
the rope will not cut itself when under strain.

A *Figure eight* prevents the rope
from being
pulled through a loop.

D *Bowline* for making a
non-slip loop
at the end of the rope.

B *Thumb knot* prevents
the rope from twisting.

E *Clove hitch* used in
mooring boats.

C *Reef knot* for joining
two ropes
of the same diameter.

F *Sheep shank* is used for
shortening a rope
that is tied at both ends.

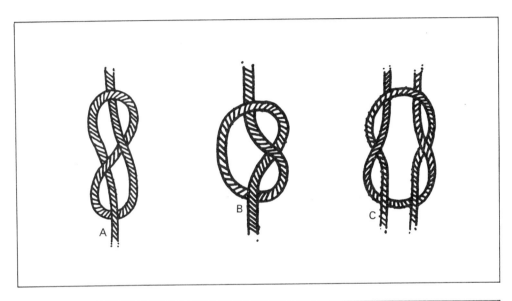

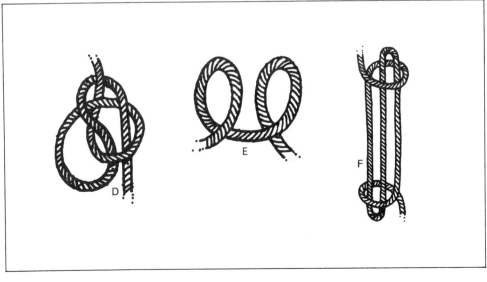

Signals

If you are lost or are involved in an air crash it is very useful to know the following signalling procedure:

Smoke and Fire
These are natural signals, easy to use and very useful. Smoke is excellent on clear fairly calm days but works anytime. Fire and smoke will provide 24-hour service.

Method
a) In accordance with the diagram, make three signal fires at least 100 feet apart if possible, and grouped in a triangle. Three fires, or signals in groups of three, are international distress calls.

b) Along a creek bank or ravine, three fires in a line work.

c) Build signal fires in an open area, a field, marshy ground, or on rafts out on a lake or pond, if possible, and close to your shelter so a quick dash can be made to light them when an aircraft is heard.

d) Have fires protected from rain and all ready to light with dry feather sticks and splintered kindling in the centre. Place larger sticks around the kindling in tepee fashion and thatch with green boughs or moss. Keep additional fuel, green boughs, moss and grass handy as emergency insurance.

e) If you are near a crashed aircraft, rubber and oil from it make a good black smoke.

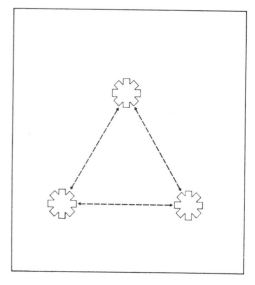

f) Smoke signal fires can be lit once a day to attract any local people in the area — forest ranger, campers and rescurers, who may see your smoke during the day or fires at night and investigate.

g) Continuous burning is unnecessary and wasteful on wood and energy.

h) Always be careful with fire and ensure that precautions are taken against your fires spreading.

Light Signals

Any form of light can be used. Camp fires, flashlights, candles or dry grass may provide a means of being detected from the air at night. A good trick is to employ a light inside a tepee or tent which lights up like a giant Japanese lantern.

Torch Tree

a) Select an evergreen tree with thick foliage, one that is isolated from other trees to minimize the risk of forest fire.

b) In winter, shake the tree or hammer the base and remove as much snow and ice as possible.

c) Build a "bird's nest" in the lower branches of the tree using branches of other trees with dry kindling and bark mixed with them.

d) Around the base of the tree prepare a bonfire – using feather sticks, dry splintered wood, bark, and any combustible material (like gas and oil from the aircraft if available).

e) This bonfire will burn and ignite the "bird's nest" which helps fire up the whole tree making it a gigantic torch – visible to aircraft and anyone for many miles around.

f) Prepare this signal in advance and use precautions against getting the kindling wet or spreading fires.

Flash Fires

If gas and oil are available, use only when the aircraft is sighted. Pour the fuel on the ground or saturate pieces of fabric and light them when needed. Take fire precautions.

Aircraft Landing Lights

Use these if they are still serviceable. Aircraft Parts – The aircraft itself is an excellent signal. Cut down nearby trees and shrubs that may conceal it from the air. Keep it clear of snow. Shiny pieces of metal from the aircraft laid on the ground will reflect the sun.

Heliograph Mirror

A very useful, important and easy to carry piece of equipment, this device has probably been responsible for effecting more rescues than other methods. It is simply a mirror with a hole in the centre so that the reflected light can be aimed accurately at the searchers. It is in nearly all types of survival kits. Follow the instructions on the back of the mirror. It can be seen many miles away on a clear sunny day. If you have no mirror, improvise with a piece of polished metal. The side of a ration can makes a good usable mirror.

Carefully cut a cross about 1 inch long in the centre of the sheet with the point of your knife while the metal is lying on a flat surface. At night a flash-light or candle light directed at the heliograph mirror may be effective.

Regular heliograph mirrors have instructions printed on the back. In case you must improvise a mirror, however, the principles involved are repeated here.

Using the Heliograph Mirror

1 Holding the mirror a few inches from your eye, face it approximately halfway between the sun and the rescue plane.

2 Intercept the sunlight that is passing through the cross in the mirror so that the cross pattern falls on your hand or other part of your person.

3 Tilt the mirror so that the cross pattern on your hand is reflected in the back of the mirror, as close as possible to the centre, where the cross is cut.

4 While sighting the rescuer through the centre of the cross, tilt the mirror so that the reflected image falls directly on the centre of the cross. The signal is now aimed directly at the rescuer.

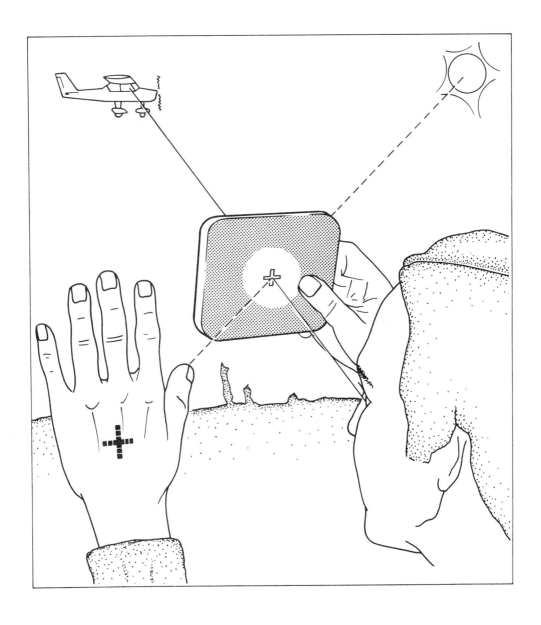

Ground to Air Signals
Use strips of fabric, parachutes, peeled logs,
stones, sod, branches in snow. Try to provide maximum contrast. All figures should
be at least 40 feet long.

Symbol	#	Meaning
▬▬ ▬	1	Require Doctor, Serious Injuries
▬▬ ▬▬	2	Require Medical Supplies
X	3	Unable to Proceed
F	4	Require Food and Water
⌄⌄	5	Require Firearms and Ammunition
□	6	Require Map and Compass
▬ ▬ ▬	7	Require Signal Lamp with Battery, and Radio
K	8	Indicate Direction to Proceed
→	9	Am Proceeding in this Direction

⊳	10	Will Attempt Take-Off
⌐	11	Aircraft Seriously Damaged
△	12	Probably Safe to Land Here
L	13	Require Fuel and Oil
LL	14	All Well
N	15	No
Y	16	Yes
⊥	17	Not Understood
W	18	Require Engineer

Shadow

Shadow signals are quite effective when built in a clearing and of sufficient size and contrast. In Canada a cross with arms running NE SW and NW SE will catch maximum sun shadow.

Construction

a) Arctic Winter – snow block wall – line the blocks along the trench from which the snow blocks were cut.
b) Arctic Summer – sod, stones, sand, or driftwood walls.
c) Bush Winter – tramped in the snow; lay green bough signals in the snow; or better still stick them in snow and build a wall of brush and boughs around them.
d) Bush Summer – rock pile signals – bush or logs for letters. Use fresh peeled logs and bark or sod blocks.

Informative Signals

If you are in an aircraft which makes a forced landing, leave a written note for a search party if you leave the crash scene or last camp site and are on the move. Write pertinent facts: date, direction travelling, number and condition of the party. Leave the message in a bottle or can, if possible, and suspend from a tree, or under a rock cairn. A sign visible from the air should be laid out also to give the direction of travel. For yourself and searcher, blaze a trail. *Note:* Check travel notes for blazing trails and leaving messages.

Conclusion

Establishing contact with or attracting the attention of searchers and rescurers should be your main objective as soon as your vital survival needs have been taken care of.

a) Have your signals all ready and show them effectively.
b) Prepare as many types of signals as you can at the best possible sites.
c) Protect signals and equipment from moisture and cold.
d) Remember that any unusual sign or colour contrast is visible from the air, even a single trail in the snow.
c) Use guns sparingly and with caution.
f) Smoke and a mirror are your best signals when no radio is available.
g) Care for your signalling equipment – learn to use it and be found.

Travel

As suggested earlier, it is not recommended that you should attempt to leave the crash site. Depending on your particular circumstances, however, there may be strong reasons for considering this option: leaving a bad campsite for a good, safe, dry location; moving to a location with good visibility; walking out to a nearby road or settlement.

Before you decide to travel, re-examine the following five conditions. If they cannot all be fulfilled, then don't travel.

1 Know where you are, and where you are going.
2 Have a means of setting and maintaining direction.
3 Make a careful, conservative estimate of your physical condition and stamina.
4 Make certain you are properly clothed. Sturdy boots are absolutely essential, and if you do not have heavy-duty working or hiking boots in summer, or proper insulated footwear such as army style mukluks in winter, don't travel.
5 Can you carry enough food, fuel, shelter and signals with you, or find them along the route? If not, don't travel.

Bush Travel in Summer
Bush travel in summer is relatively easy, if the following rules are followed:

1 Before beginning any trip, climb a high hill or large tree to orient yourself with the surrounding area and possibly discover human habitation.

2 Game trails provide an easy path through bush country. These trails follow the ridges and river flats and are connected by a network of trails. The danger in following these trails extensively may cause you to wander from your intended direction.

3 Streams may be followed to larger rivers or lakes, along the shores of which you are most likely to find habitation. Generally, it is better to follow the drainage pattern rather than cross it. Unless the waterways in the area are well known to the survivors, raft building is not recommended.

4 Ridges offer drier, more insect-free travel than bottom land. There will usually be less underbush and as a result it will be easier to see and be seen.

The wilderness raft
Built without nails or rope

Raft assembled

A Cross pieces
They should fit loosely. They will
swell when wet.

B Steering sweep
Made from a green pole. Small end split
to take oar blade.

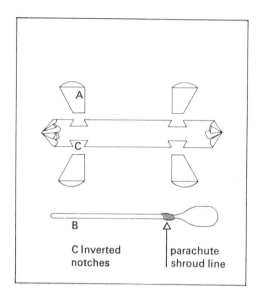

C Inverted
notches

parachute
shroud line

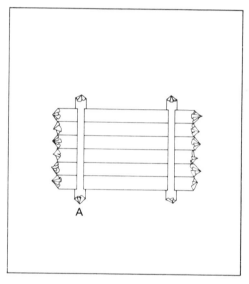

5 Large river crossing should be attempted
only when absolutely necessary. If the water
is deep, remove all clothing and place it in a
bundle. Replace your boots without socks.
Boots give a much better footing and prevent injury to your feet during the crossing.
If forced to swim in fast flowing rivers, start
up-stream from your proposed landing place
and let the current drift you down to it. When
fording a fast shallow stream use a pole to
help you maintain a footing.

6 Decide whether to cross or go around each
lake. If it is decided to cross, use a raft or
flotation gear. Swimming in cold waters can
be treacherous.

7 Deadfalls can prove dangerous because
of the ever present danger of slipping, resulting in injury. Swamps sap the strength
of a person because of difficult walking
conditions. Go around such areas.

8 Mountain areas have their own particular
problems. Watch for overhead threats such
as shale and rolling boulders. In early spring,
cross mountain streams in early morning
to avoid the greatest volume of water
which occurs when the sun starts melting
the snows.

Bush Travel in Winter

In winter game trails, especially if heavily used, will save walking through deep snow, but you must avoid being led off your general direction. Streams and rivers will provide your best method of travel, being the highways of the Canadian north. There are, however, dangers in winter river travel which must be carefully watched for and avoided. In certain places along the river, weak ice will be found, and it is best to know in advance where to look for it.

1 Stay away from rocks and other protrusions, since ice is slower to form in these localities and will have been retarded by eddies.

2 Walk on the inside of curves, since on the outside of curves the river current has an eroding effect on the under side of the ice surfaces.

3 Take to the bank or walk on the opposite side of the river at the junction of two rivers. The current from both rivers holds up the formation of ice through turbulence.

4 Stay on clear ice when possible since a deep layer of snow will insulate and retard freezing.

5 Carry a pole for testing ice and for use in supporting your weight if you break through the ice.

6 Be prepared to get rid of your pack if you should fall through the ice.

Ridges may give easier walking conditions as they do not usually have the same amount of snow as the valleys. Mountain areas, in winter, can be particularly treacherous, with the possibility of snow slides, uncertain footing and sudden storms. Snow slides will occur from natural causes, but care should be taken to avoid causing them through carelessness. Deadfall is even more dangerous in winter than in summer since a lot of it will be covered with snow, making walking conditions very treacherous.

Emergency Snowshoes

It is extremely difficult to travel in deep snow without some kind of skis or snowshoes. Skis need not be a problem if ingenuity is exercised. Snowshoes can be constructed from evergreen branches. Start by tying a good, sturdy branch into an oval frame, using whatever materials are available to secure it. Other branches are placed across the frame and tied. Interweaving the cross branches will give extra strength and rigidity.

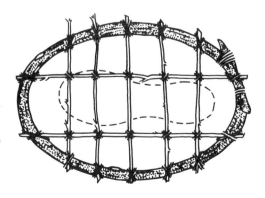

Barren Land Travel

Show shoes and skis are not essential on hard snow in barren land travel. On the Arctic Islands and barrens east of the 142nd meridian, walking conditions are normally good in winter. In some localities frequent gales are encountered. There is little protection except that provided by scattered high banks and willow thickets around lakes and along stream beds. Game is very scarce and fires cannot be maintained for long on the fuel obtainable in the winter. The survivors cannot afford to follow the streams, which, because of their winding nature, double and quadruple the distance to be covered. The compass is not reliable and landmarks are few and far between. One man will have difficulty steering a straight course by himself. Two can do a little better but three are required to navigate when visibility is low. It is recommended that any extended travel over barren or sea ice be done by a party of at least three.

The spring break-up, summer and the fall freeze present far greater travel difficulties than does the winter season. Equipment must be carried on the back. The masses of soggy vegetation on the tundra cause the traveller to slip and slide. Lake systems must be either crossed or circumnavigated. Care must be taken in crossing sandbars and mud flats formed at the mouths and junctions of rivers and lakes. Quicksands or bottomless muck may trap you. If a life raft is available, it is preferable to float down the river rather than attempt to travel across country. The months of July and August are about the best months for cross country travel. Because of the prevalence of fish in all streams or lakes, a fish net is one of the best pieces of equipment the traveller can carry. A rifle may provide game for a number of meals.

Sea Ice Travel

Food in the form of seal, fox and polar bear is more readily obtained on winter sea ice than on barren land. The problems of navigation are identical with those on the barren lands with one very great exception. The polar ice pack is in constant motion due to the currents and winds. Therefore, determination of direction may be difficult. Also one rarely travels in a straight line, in order to avoid the rough ice. Landmarks in the form of high pressure ridges and hummocks are usable only for short distances, since they may be located on other floes and are constantly changing location. Add to this fact that the magnetic compass is very unreliable in high latitudes and the necessity for constant directional checks on the sun and stars become obvious.

The ice in the very high latitudes is comparatively solid in winter. As the sun returns the ice recedes and there is open water along the entire Arctic coast. Along the north coast, ice lies off shore and is often driven ashore by strong north or west winds Riding one of these floes is definitely a last and dangerous procedure, since there is no guarantee that the wind will continue until the floe reaches ground.

The summer ice is covered with lakes and water soaked snow, which gradually drains off through holes and cracks in the ice mass. There is practically no dry surface anywhere. Fogs abound and misting rain falls frequently. Survivors should leave the ice and get to land if at all possible.

All icebergs frozen in the ice are likely to have open water in their vicinity. Icebergs driven by the wind and currents have been known to crash through ice several feet in thickness. Towering icebergs in open water are always dangerous as the area below the surface melts faster than that above causing it to topple over and the adjoining area is no place for man or beast. The resulting tidal waves throw the surrounding small ice pieces in all directions. Seek only low topped icebergs for shelter at sea.

Messages

Messages should be left at every stop. A
message should also be left at any point at
which a change of plans is put into effect.
The message should contain the following
information:

a) date of leaving original point
b) destination and route
c) estimated length of the journey
d) number in the party
e) physical condition of the party
f) any other pertinent data

Make certain the message is left in a readily
accessible place. Lacking a pencil or pen,
messages may be written with charcoal, a
stick or finger dipped in oil or grease.

Turn left (Stones)

Turn right

Broken sapling —
Direction of trail indicated.

Markers with stones

Direction Finding

Using the Compass to Travel

Strap or clamp the compass on a sled with one runner of the sled running in the direction of travel. The box of the compass should be parallel to the side of the sled. Rotate the compass housing so that the track required is opposite the index pointer. Now read your required track which is opposite the index pointer.

Send a member of your party two to three hundred yards ahead and in line with the compass reading. Move forward with the sled to the member's location at which time he will advance another two hundred yards.

Almost as accurate travel may be accomplished by travelling both at the same time about one hundred yards apart with sled driver directing the leader to keep him in line with the compass reading.

Reading the Compass Using a Map

The magnetic needle is read between the two luminous lines by its reflection in the sighting mirror. In using the sighting mirror, you can see that, when the needle is oriented between the two parallel lines, it appears to be closer to one line than to the other. This is due to the mirror being placed at a 41° angle and produced this reflexion according to the laws of parallax. In sighting, parallel the needle with the orienting line which appears nearest it and keep the compass level.

Map Reading

While it may not be possible for you to learn all the symbols shown on various maps, it is well to know those which indicate difficult or impossible travel or arid locations. Generally speaking these are as follows:

a) *Swamps or Marches.* The dotted lines indicate that the exact shore line of the marsh or swamp is not known.

b) *Undulating Country.* The height of the ground is indicated by a continuous line joining all points of equal height. The variation in height will differ depending on the scale of the map and the terrain which it covers.

c) *Rapids.* These are shown as a series of light lines drawn across the river covering the area in which the rapids occur. They are usually marked only on navigable rivers.

d) *Falls.* These are generally shown as a light double line drawn directly across a river, with the word "falls" written alongside, and a figure indicating the drop in feet.

e) *Trails.* These are usually shown as dotted lines, either single or double. A single line usually denotes a pack trail, while double lines usually indicate a trail used by wagons or tractors.

1 *Right:* The magnetic needle is closer to one line than to the other.

2 *Wrong:* The magnetic needle appears to be centred between the two luminous lines.

3 Line of travel

4 *Contour Lines.* This shows that a steep slope is represented by contour lines close together while a shallow slope has contour lines far apart.

1.

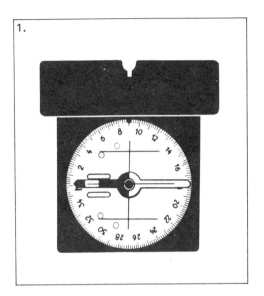

2.

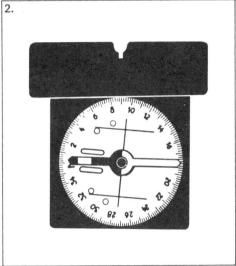

3.

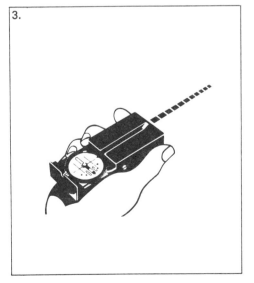

4.

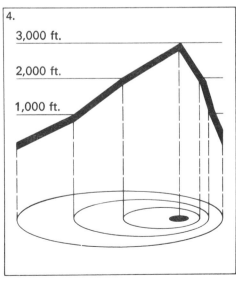

3,000 ft.

2,000 ft.

1,000 ft.

1 *Falls.* These are generally shown as a light double line drawn across a river.

2 *Rapids.* These are shown as a series of light lines drawn across the river.

3 *Swamps or Marshes.* The dotted line indicates that the exact shore line of the marsh or swamp is not known.

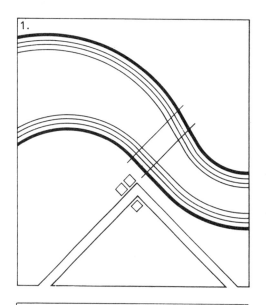

1.

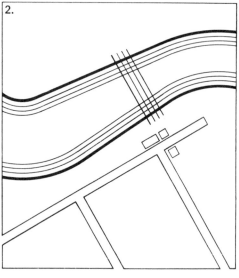

2.

3.

f) *Cabins.* Ranger stations, etc., are marked as black squares with "Cabin", "Mission", or "Lookout Tower" written alongside. Trading posts are shown as black squares with TR written alongside.

It is best to remember that the shortest distance between two points is not necessarily the quickest route. Pick your route carefully to give you easy walking conditions, even if it does add a few miles to the trip. It will pay off in the long run.

Finding Direction without a Compass
Three methods of finding North are discussed here.

Using the sun and a watch to determine a north-south line

Point the hour hand directly at the sun. Then by bisecting the angle between the hour hand and twelve o'clock you have an imaginary line running north and south.

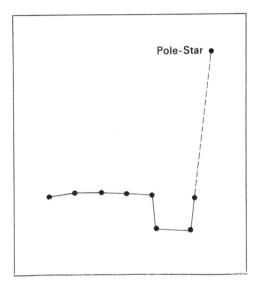

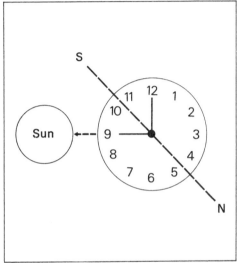

The first, by using the pole-star, is the easiest. Having found the pole-star, simply face it and you are facing North. To find the pole-star, the Big Dipper or Plough is used.

The second method uses the sun and a watch to find true North. Hold the watch flat in the hand. Place a match or straw upright along the edge of the watch. Turn the watch until the shadow of the match falls directly along the hour hand, that is, until the hour hand points directly at the sun. Between the hours of 6 a.m. and 6 p.m. standard time a line from the centre of the watch, dividing the small angle between the hour hand and the figure 12 will point South. Between 6 p.m. and 6 a.m. divide the large angle to find South.

Remember, in the Arctic when the sun is up all day, any confusion between 12 and midnight and 12 noon could cause a 180 degree error in direction. In the example shown above, had the observation been at 8 p.m. rather than 8 a.m., the direction would be reversed. Make certain your watch is on standard time when taking readings.

The third method of finding north is to place a long stick in the ground, and as the sun progresses place shorter twigs in the ground at the end of the shadows at intervals of fifteen minutes or more. Draw a straight line A along the line of short twigs and this will indicate east and west. North will therefore be found by drawing a line B at right angles to line A.

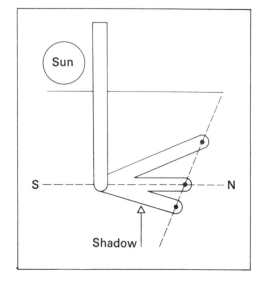

Sun

S — — — — — — — — — — — — N

Shadow

General Reference

Arctic Manual
Vilhjalmur Stefansson,
Macmillan Company, New York.

Comparison of climate and accessibility
of Churchill, Manitoba and Fairbanks, Alaska
U.S. Air Force,
Arctic Aeromedical Laboratory.

Down But Not Out
Information Canada,
Ottawa, Canada.

Down in the North
R. H. Howard,
Maxwell Air Force Base.

Edible Plants in the North
U.S. Air Force,
Arctic Aeromedical Laboratory.

Emergency Living in the Arctic
New York training aids division.

Fat of the Land
Vilhjalmur Stefansson,
Macmillan Company, New York.

Friendly Arctic
Vilhjalmur Stefansson,
Macmillan Company, New York.

Guides Manual
Ontario Department of Lands and Forests,
Parliament Buildings, Toronto, Ontario.

Man in the Arctic
Harley J. Walker,
Maxwell Air Force Base.

Procurement of Animals, Birds, Fish
in the Arctic and Sub Arctic
Arctic Desert Tropic Information Centre.

Search-Rescue-Survival
The R.C.A.F. Rescue Co-ordination Centre,
Winnipeg, Manitoba.

Small Group Performance
under Isolation and Distress
U.S. Air Force,
Arctic Aeromedical Laboratory.

So You Want To Go Camping
Ontario Department of Lands and Forests,
Parliament Buildings, Toronto, Ontario.

Survival Hints For The Sportsman
R.C.A.F. Air Transport Command,
Trenton, Ontario.

Survival in the Woods
Ontario Department of Lands and Forests,
Parliament Buildings, Toronto, Ontario.

Your Emergency Survival Kit
Civil Defence Department,
Milwaukee, Wisconsin, U.S.A.